CW00664888

The Bumblebees of Essex

The Bumblebees of Essex

by

Ted Benton

 Lopinga Books

Published by Lopinga Books
Tye Green House, Wimbish, GB-Essex, CB10 2XE

In association with, and in support of the work of, the
Essex Field Club and the Colchester Natural History Society

With financial support from Environment Agency and
English Nature

First published 2000

Text, drawings, maps & photographs © Ted Benton

Chapter 9 compiled by David Corke (see credits at head of chapter)

Front cover painting © Alan Harris, 2000

ISBN 0-9530362-4-3

British Library Cataloguing-in-Publication Data
A catalogue record for this book is available from the British Library

Designed by Lopinga Books

Printed by Healeys Printers Ltd, Unit 10, The Sterling Complex, Ipswich IP1 5AP

The *Nature of Essex Series* No. 4

Contents

When a group of animals or plants is the subject of a book treating it at county level, the group has surely come of age in terms of popularity. Wild-flowers achieved this status early with the publication of John Ray's *Flora of Cambridgeshire* in 1660 (Ewen & Prime, 1975). Wild flowers were followed by other popular groups such as birds, butterflies and dragonflies. It is pleasing to see that bumblebees have now made the grade. This book deals with 20 of the 25 species on the British list, omitting only two that are probably extinct and three species with a northern and western distribution. It will enhance the studies of amateur and professional bombologists by outlining what is already known of the natural history of each species, and pointing to further investigations that are needed. It will strengthen the basis for the conservation of these important pollinators by highlighting changes in their distribution, identifying areas and habitats of special value, and showing how we might meet the habitat requirements of declining species.

The book will be an invaluable tool and inspiration for those interested in bumblebees far beyond the boundaries of its focal county, and will surely stimulate a surge of interest in bumblebee research and conservation.

Sarah Corbet

Dr Sarah A Corbet

Department of Zoology
University of Cambridge

Acknowledgements vii

I am particularly grateful to Mike Edwards of the UK Bumblebee Working Group, George R. Else and Dr Paul H. Williams at the Natural History Museum, London, and Dr Sarah Corbet for freely sharing their great expertise with me. The staff of the Entomology Library at the Natural History Museum provided indispensable bibliographical help.

No less valuable has been the help and support given locally by P.R. Harvey, J. Firmin, R.G. Payne, J.P. Bowdrey, J.J. Heath, C.W. Plant, Dr C. Gibson and fellow Essex entomologists. More widely, membership of the Essex Field Club and Colchester Natural History Society has provided me with a unique experience of both convivial and expert companionship without which this work would never have been even contemplated. T. Tarpey gave invaluable help with my 'virtual' computer skills, and the encouragement of example. Mrs N. Chapman very kindly loaned me a file of her late husband's (Dr D.I. Chapman) Hymenoptera records. Most of my field-work was accomplished by public transport or on foot, but offers of transport to the more remote parts of the county by C. Gibson, M. James, D. and A. Lee and J. Kramer were gratefully accepted. Many people contributed records during the course of this survey: M. P. Attwood, K.M. Black, J. P. Bowdrey, S. Burden, D. Corke, D.E. Deacon, D.G. Down, G.R. Else, M. Edwards, M.A. Fremlin, M.J. Gregory, M. W. Hanson, J. J. Heath, N. Harvey, P. R. Harvey, K. Hill, P. Kent, R. D. Kent, G.J. Lucas, S. Massey, G. Moore, E. Parsons, R.G. Payne, R. Pennington, S.L. Pennington, H F. Perry, C.W. Plant, the late G. A. Pyman, J. Rose, K.M. Rowland, R.D. Ruffell, D A. Smith, G. Smith, G. Wilkinon.

P.R. Harvey provided many records, especially from the south of the county, gave much of the information used in chapter 4, and contributed in many other ways to the completion of this work. D. Corke has been an exemplary editor and publisher, correcting numerous errors and giving invaluable advice.

The following were kind enough to read and comment on all or parts of the manuscript: Dr S.A. Corbet, M. Edwards, Dr G.R. Else, Dr C. Gibson, P.R. Harvey, S. Randolph and Dr P.H. Williams

The Essex distribution maps were generated using the DMAP software package created by Dr Alan Morton, using the Essex county boundary data compiled by P.R. Harvey. The British distribution maps were created using Paint Shop Pro software.

Sponsors

I am grateful to the organisations that provided financial support for this project, for grants from English Nature and the Environment Agency and for grant/loans from the Colchester Natural History Society and Essex Field Club. These two organisations will receive the royalties from the sale of this book.

Conventions viii

Sex and Caste: In the literature there is some confusion in the use of these terms. In this work, I generally refer to the male 'sex'. When females are referred to, the term 'female' is used for females of subgenus *Psithyrus*, or for the females of other subgenera when both workers and queens are included. When discrimination between the female castes is required, the terms 'worker' and 'queen' are used. In the bumblebees, the term 'queen' primarily refers to the role played in the colony by the dominant and reproductive female. However, in this work, the term is used more widely include also sexually developed females through from their summer emergence and hibernation to the establishment of the nests in spring. Sometimes the phrase 'young queens' is used to denote freshly emerged females, in contrast to the overwintered queens whose offspring they are.

Common versus Scientific Names: Most bumblebee species have been assigned English-language names by various authors, but these have not been standardised, and they are not in every-day use. It was therefore decided to use scientific names, except in the case of the shrill carder bee (*Bombus sylvarum*), whose English name has been popularised through its inclusion in both national and Essex Biodiversity Action Plans and some common species which have appropriate English names. The wild flowers used as forage sources do have standard vernacular names in common use, and these have been used in text descriptions and in the tables. However, the scientific equivalents are given in the Appendix. In the case of cultivated plants, however, the situation is much more confused, some plants being known by vernacular and others by scientific terms. Even more problematic has been the identification of cultivated plants. Since most observations have been made by looking over garden hedges and fences (!) it has often been possible to identify genera, but not species or variety. Clearly from the point of view of conservation this would be of great value, but with the limitations of this survey (and its author) the best that could be done is the very provisional alphabetical list of genera (with a few distinctive species) given in the Appendix.

True and Cuckoo Bumblebees: From the point of view of field observation, it is useful to retain this distinction, since the parasitic way of life, lack of division of labour between queens and workers, and lack of a corbiculum separate out the 'cuckoos' from all other bumblebees. However, it is now accepted that the old practice of assigning them to a separate genus is unjustified from a scientific/evolutionary point of view. In this work, the scientific case is respected by referring to *Psithyrus* as a subgenus of *Bombus*. However, the old distinction continues to be marked by the English-language phrases 'true' and 'cuckoo' bumblebees where this is appropriate.

Abbreviations: Recorders mentioned in the course of the text are referred to by their initials: T.B. (Ted Benton), D.G.D. (Don Down), P.R.H. (Peter Harvey), R.G.P. (Roger Payne)

This book is the result of some 15 years of field observation of bumblebees in Essex. Many other observers contributed valuable evidence, and I benefited greatly from the help of the staff of the Biological Records Centres in the county, The Natural History Museum, London, the National Bumblebee Working Group, and friends who helped in various ways – most notably by offering transport (see Acknowledgements). With the help of the Essex Biological Records Centres, I was able to include records from 1980 onwards (prior to the start of my own recording from 1985 onwards) into the distribution maps shown for each species. This gives continuity for comparative purposes with the national *Atlas of the Bumblebees of the British Isles* published by the International Bee Research Association and the Institute of Terrestrial Ecology (IBRA/ITE, 1980). However, it proved difficult to recover many of the original sources of the data used in that work, so that inferences about changes in distributions based on comparisons with it have been rather speculative. Such data as are available from the survey which led to the *Atlas* include records submitted by D.V. Alford, N. Bardell, W. Booker (Davenport School), B. Dicker, I. Goss, W. Hooper, D. Martin, D. Millar, R. Payne, G. Sagrott, P.H. Williams and N. Young.

So far as the Essex bumblebees were concerned, relatively little work had been done prior to the current survey. W.H. Harwood and his sons collected extensively in the Colchester area around a century ago, and many of their specimens are in The Natural History Museum (London). C. Nicholson worked on the aculeate Hymenoptera, including bumblebees, in the 1920s, and D.I. Chapman collated the work of earlier entomologists, complementing it with field observations of his own during the 1960s. From the point of view of determining the current status of the rare or local species the only guide provided by the *Atlas* in most cases was a 10 km square grid reference. Given the enormous changes which have occurred in the Essex countryside in recent decades, as a result of agricultural intensification, building development, road construction and other causes, the task of reliably ascertaining the continued presence or extinction of what may have been small, localised bee populations seemed daunting.

My first two or three seasons of study were devoted to the task of learning to identify the castes of each of the commoner species in the field. This did entail making a small reference collection, but my aim was to study 'jizz' sufficiently well to carry out reliable field recording without killing the bees. There were two reasons for this. One was a simple reluctance to kill unless it was absolutely necessary. The second was that I wanted to make detailed observations of the behaviour of the bees in the field. This clearly ruled out catching and killing them, yet the observations would have little value unless they could be attributed to species and, preferably, to caste.

However, the workers of some species, especially, are difficult to tell apart, and in some species the castes are not clearly distinguishable without close examination. My compromise in such cases was to catch some individuals for close examination in the field, and then release them. The technique I used for this generally dispensed with the net (especially useless when bees are foraging on brambles or thistles!). Instead I used a 2.5 cm by 5 cm glass or plastic tube. While intent on foraging bees are easily caught by placing the open end of the tube over them and quickly replacing the stopper. Their movements can be restricted by gradually opening the tube and inserting a wad of cotton wool or paper tissue. This can be used to press the bee gently against the base or side of the tube, while diagnostic features are checked with a x10 hand lens. The bee can then be released unharmed. Sometimes it is hard to avoid dislodging pollen loads, but otherwise the technique does not seem to harm the bees – they often return directly to foraging where they left off.

From the late 1980s onwards, my fieldwork was devoted to two main aims. The first was to extend my field recording to those parts of Essex, which were, up to that time, under-recorded. The second was to carry out much more focussed explorations of likely habitat for the rarer and more localised species. So far as the first aim was concerned, my recording was carried out on a 1 km square basis, but I aimed initially for even coverage of the county on a 10 km square basis, to enable comparison with the IBRA/ITE atlas. Since I was also carrying out behavioural observations in the Colchester area, it seemed unrealistic to establish evenness of coverage across the county in terms of similar numbers of visits to each grid square. Instead, I adopted the provisional 'base-line' of regarding six species of *Bombus*, and one species of (what was then treated as the separate genus) *Psithyrus* as ubiquitous in the county. I would not count any 10 km square as adequately covered until I had recorded at least these seven species in it (see Williams, 2000). This required many repeat-visits to such squares over subsequent years, so that by the end of the survey (with the help of other observers) I had almost comprehensive coverage to the 5 km square level. The maps are generally presented here on a tetrad basis, as a compromise between the 5 km level and the 1 km square basis of the actual recording.

The second aim, a more focussed search for the rarer and more localised species, was initially directed to the coastal grazing marshes of east Essex. These seem to provide the only Essex habitat for the localised carder bee *Bombus muscorum*. Extensive searches for *Bombus sylvarum* (the shrill carder bee), recorded from north-east Essex in the IBRA/ITE survey, proved fruitless, and I was coming to the conclusion that it was extinct in the county. However, Peter Harvey's discovery of the species in south Essex in 1993 led to more extensive searches, by several observers, of uncultivated biotopes along the Thames estuary. These searches revealed a number of sites for both *B. sylvarum*, and another localised and declining bumblebee, *Bombus humilis*. Alarmingly, some of the best of these sites were threatened by development pressures and some have already been destroyed (Harvey, 1999a, 2000).

Other Essex rarites, or declining species, (*Bombus ruderatus, B. ruderarius* and *B. (Psithyrus) rupestris*) have no obvious specialised habitat requirements, and were recorded incidentally, as part of the routine 'square bashing'. One other species, *B. subterraneus*, was recorded from the county prior to 1980, but was not re-found during the current survey. It is now considered to be extinct in Britain.

In the last three years of the survey (1997-99) more systematic records were made of flight times of each species and caste, together with notes of their forage sources at different times of year. The results of these observations make interesting comparisons both with those of observers earlier in the century, and with those of Fussell & Corbet (1991, 1993). The Essex observations show much longer flight seasons for some species than the existing literature suggests. The possibility here is that more species are double- (even triple-) brooded than earlier authors have supposed, and there is some evidence of over-wintering colonies. Connected with this, the Essex data indicate the great importance for some bumblebees of a small number of species of forage-plants that provide nourishment both very early and late in the season. For those species that are able to make regular use of gardens and public parks, the extended flowering periods of many alien and cultivated varieties may be a significant factor, along with climate change, in lengthening their flight period into the winter months. The Essex data also complement, in interesting ways, the findings of Fussell & Corbet (1991) on the significance of agricultural practices for bumblebees as pollinators of agricultural crops.

Fortuitously, these final years of the survey coincided with the establishment of a national Bumblebee Working Group under the leadership of Michael Edwards. This group had been set up in the light of growing evidence of a rapid decline of several British bumblebee species. Of the five species initially selected for special attention at the national level, no fewer than three have been recorded in Essex during the current survey: *Bombus sylvarum, B. humilis* and *B. ruderatus*. In collaboration with the national Working Group, Peter Harvey (Essex Field Club recorder of Hymenoptera), Roger Payne of the Southend Museum and other specialists, field work was focussed on identifying the localities, habitat requirements, foraging and nesting behaviour of, and threats to, these species (see Edwards 1997, 1998 & 1999). This work has added considerably to current knowledge of at least two of these species (*B. sylvarum* and *B. humilis*) but many mysteries remain!

Finally, just as this book was being prepared for the printers, the author found a queen of *B. jonellus*, apparently the first record for this species in the county, and bringing the total number of species recorded during the survey up to 17.

Bumblebees have a firm place in public affection and in the artistic imagination. They are among the earliest insects to emerge from winter hibernation, and for many of us the sight of the massive queens of black-and-yellow-banded bumblebees (usually *Bombus terrestris*) eagerly probing the catkins of early-flowering sallow bushes has come to symbolise the arrival of spring. Later in the year, the hordes of worker bees can fill the air with their soft buzzing where the flower-rich meadows and hedgerows they frequent still survive in our industrialised agricultural landscapes. More familiar to most of us are the welcome visits they make to our garden flowers: few gardens, no matter how small and surrounded by urban development, are missed by foraging bumblebees. Perhaps it is this familiarity, together with their 'cuddly', furry appearance, and their sociability, which makes for such a popular image, by contrast with most of their fellow insects – notably the stinging and biting varieties!

The social bees have long been used as a metaphor for human society and politics. Sometimes it is the uniform, industrious workers who are praised for their self sacrifice as in the conservative writings of Mandeville (in his *Fable of the Bees*). Or it is the class division of the bee colony, with its exploited workers and leisured class of unproductive drones, which is condemned in its human version by the writers of the left , such as the romantic poet, Percy Bysshe Shelley: *'The worker bees worked; the drones lazed about and consumed what the workers produced. The wretchedness of the workers and the greed of the drones were inexorably bound together.'* (Foot, 1980). But the social bees have long been important to human society in their own right, not just as the basis for metaphorical speculation. The honeybee, of course, has long been domesticated (Crane, 2000), and was probably subject to plunder by human opportunists, as by other animal species, long before the techniques of domestication were invented.

The bumblebees, however, have never been so readily, or so profitably domesticated. Their colonies are usually smaller, and more short-lived, than those of the honeybee. However, they confer a different sort of economic benefit: they, or certain species of them at any rate, are highly efficient pollinators of a number of horticultural and agricultural crops. Studies, in Canada, the USA and many European countries, of the pollination of red clover, broad bean, oil-seed rape, lucerne, cranberry, and fruit blossom, such as apple and plum, have confirmed their economic importance.

In recent years, the impact of the *Varroa jacobsoni* mite on honeybee populations has led to concern that seed yield in many crops previously pollinated by them will suffer (Corbet, 1987; Corbet *et al.* 1991; 1993; Free, 1970b; Kevan *et al.*, 1990; Patten *et al.*, 1993). This has focussed attention on the positive role of bumblebees as pollinators: for example, in 1992 a *Daily Telegraph* headline ran*: 'Bumble bee flies to rescue of farmers'*. Unfortunately, the farmers had been doing nothing to rescue the bumblebees! There is mounting evidence of serious decline in bumblebee populations and some species are now believed extinct, or very nearly so, in the UK. The principal culprit seems to be the mechanisation of agriculture, with the ploughing or 'improvement' of flower-rich meadows, the removal of hedgerows, and the generally more intensive utilisation of land. Research suggests that bumblebees are particularly dependent on large areas of flower-rich habitat for the large numbers of foraging workers that may be produced by each nest. They also need suitable undisturbed banks, headlands or ditches for the establishment of nests and for hibernation (Williams, 1982, 1985, 1988, 1989a, 1989b). Successful production of fresh males and young queens requires a succession of plants to supply nectar and pollen throughout the flight period. Available forage plants in the early spring and late in the summer may be a critical factor in the survival of some species.

There are economic as well as good sentimental reasons for the expression of official concern in the face of mounting evidence of the alarming decline in populations of bumblebees. The 'Earth Summit' which took place at Rio in 1992 highlighted the loss of biodiversity as a matter of intense global concern (Grubb *et al.*, 1993). One spin-off was the drawing-up of a UK Biodiversity Action Plan (Department of Environment, 1994) and the establishment of a Steering Group of scientists, conservationists and planners to develop plans for the selection and protection of key species and habitats in the UK (UK Biodiversity Steering Group, 1995, 1999). No fewer than five species of bumblebees were included in the Plan, and a UK Bumblebee Working Group was set up, with representation from the Countryside Council for Wales, English Nature, Scottish Natural Heritage, the World Wide Fund for Nature and the RSPB. As already mentioned, three of these BAP species currently occur in Essex, whilst a fourth was found in the county until the relatively recent past. Both *B. humilis* and *B. sylvarum* have nationally important populations in Essex.

Bumblebees, and their relative the honeybee, belong to the vast insect order known as the Hymenoptera. There are a few wingless Hymenoptera (*e.g.* the worker castes among the ants), but most members of this order have two pairs of fully developed wings. The hind wings are usually considerably smaller than the front wings, and are connected to them by rows of minute hooks along the wing margins. The wings are not covered with scales (as in the Lepidoptera – butterflies and moths) or hairs (as in the Trichoptera – caddis-flies), but are usually more-or-less transparent (though sometimes with cloudy coloured suffusions). Unlike dragonflies (Odonata) and the lacewings (Neuroptera), the wings have relatively few cross-veins.

The Hymenoptera are divided into two main groups, the Symphyta and the Apocrita. The Symphyta are the sawflies, which include some serious pests of cereal and fruit crops, as well as the large and striking black-and-yellow horntail, or 'woodwasp' (*Urocerus gigas*). The Apocrita include two not very well defined groups: the Parasitica, of which the best known are the parasitic ichneumons, and the Aculeata (bees, wasps and ants). The Apocrita can be distinguished from the sawflies by the constriction in the former of the body (the 'waist') behind the thorax.

Distinguishing the various groups among the bees, wasps and ants is quite technical, and is beyond the scope of this book. Within each of the main groups, some species have evolved as social animals. This means that there is co-operation between parental and offspring generations in rearing further offspring. It also involves some degree of division of labour between narrowly reproductive individuals and others which perform a variety of tasks such as foraging for siblings, nest maintenance, and defence. The ants (Formicidae) are all social, or social parasites, with some 15,000 known species in the world. Most of the wasps are solitary, but this can be a misleading term as many species of 'solitary' bees and wasps often nest in dense aggregations. However, they generally lack systematic division of labour or co-operation between the generations, but one family of wasps, the Vespidae, has several truly social species. Likewise, most species of bees are 'solitary', but members of subfamily Apinae include numerous species of social bees: the honeybee (*Apis mellifera*) and the bumblebees (genus *Bombus*). However, as with the Vespidae, some of the Apinae have evolved a parasitic way of life, invading the nests of social species and 'tricking' the host workers into rearing their offspring. These are the cuckoo bumblebees, and they used to be assigned to a separate genus, *Psithyrus*, though it has now been established that they should be classified as a sub-group within the genus *Bombus* (see Williams, 1994). This book, and the survey on which it is based, includes both groups as 'bumblebees'.

However, the old practice of distinguishing the 'cuckoo' bumblebees from the 'true' bumblebees continues to be useful for the field naturalist. The lack of a worker caste and their status as social parasites in the nests of true bumblebees set cuckoo bumblebees apart in ways that are ecologically and behaviourally significant. In the rest of this book the distinction will be marked by the use of the vernacular 'true' and 'cuckoo' bumblebees, whilst conforming to the scientific consensus that *Psithyrus* should now be included within the enlarged genus *Bombus*.

The structure of bumblebees

The body of an adult bumblebee, as with all typical insects, is divided into three main sections: a head, thorax and abdomen (fig. 5.9). There are three pairs of jointed legs, which are attached to the thorax, and two pairs of wings. The body is covered with a more-or-less dense coat of hairs, the colour and pattern of which are useful guides to field identification.

The head has two large compound eyes, and, on the 'forehead', three simple eyes or ocelli. There is one pair of antennae, which have twelve segments in females, thirteen in males (fig. 5.6). In some species the relative sizes of the segments and their shape is valuable for identification. The head also carries the mouthparts. These include a pair of pliar-like mandibles for biting that are not much used in feeding, but are believed to be important for defence, and also for nest-building and repairing activities. Below and between the mandibles emerges the long 'tongue', or proboscis, which the bee uses to probe the corolla of flowers to reach and suck up nectar. This apparatus is folded back under the bee's body when it is not in use.

The thorax is made up of three segments, to which are attached the legs and wings. The structure of the legs is as shown in fig. 5.3. In females of the social species of *Bombus*, the hind legs are modified for the collection of pollen for the brood. The most obvious feature is that the hind tibiae are flattened and hairless on the outer surface, with a fringe of long, curved hairs at the sides. These form the 'pollen basket' or corbiculum. At the junction of the tibia and the basitarsus is a structure (the 'propodium') through which pollen grains are forced into the corbiculum as the bee forages. When a foraging bee returns to the nest it detaches its pollen load by a slicing movement over the corbicula using the tarsi of the mid-legs. The males of the social species also generally have a flattened and more-or-less shiny and hairless outer surface of the hind tibia. In the social parasitic species both sexes have convex and hairy outer surfaces to the hind tibiae.

The wings are membranous, and more-or-less transparent, with relatively few veins. They are controlled in flight by powerful muscles attached to the inner wall of the thorax. The thorax wall also has pairs of small holes, or spiracles, which are used for breathing, but are also modified to produce the bee's 'buzz', which is subsequently amplified by wing vibrations.

The abdomen consists of a series of hardened segments, connected by more flexible membranes and muscles. One segment attaches the abdomen to the thorax, and others conceal the sex organs. For convenience, the segments are numbered according to the visible ones only. There are six of these in the females and seven in males. The upper or dorsal plates of the abdomen are known as tergites, the lower or ventral ones as sternites. In the females of the social species there are cells which produce wax attached to some of the tergites and sternites. The wax is secreted onto the surface of the abdomen and scraped off with the hind legs, and is then used in the construction of brood-cells or other structures in the nest. The side walls of the abdomen also have pairs of spiracles used for breathing. In queens, prior to hibernation, the abdomen contains a large collection of cells, the 'fat body', which contains fat, sugar and protein as a food-reserve for the winter. This body is almost exhausted in the spring. At the tip of the abdomen are the main reproductive organs. In females the egg-laying apparatus has been modified to form the sting. In dead specimens this can be pulled out with forceps to expose the underlying 'sting-sheath' (fig. 5.12 a-d). This differs in structure from species to species and can be used in identification (see figs 5.10

and 5.31). The ovaries of workers and queens in the autumn and winter are thin and thread-like. However, with increased nourishment and activity in the spring those of the queens enlarge and develop, ready for egg-laying once a nest-site has been established. The male external reproductive organs form a hard 'capsule' contained within an opening at the tip of the abdomen. In dead specimens this can be extruded by applying pressure to the abdomen, and examined microscopically (figs 5.4 and 5.11). Again, the structure of the male genital capsule is often the most useful feature for definitive identification (see figs 5.32 and 5.34).

The body of adult bumblebees is almost entirely covered with a coat of hair. Since the outer cuticle of the bee is black, the colour patterns of the various species are produced by pigmentation of the hairy coat. In many species, the pattern of black and yellow coloration serves as a 'warning' to potential predators, and is an example of Müllerian mimicry. It is thought that bees with this warning pattern will benefit from similarities with others (because this will make learning more rapid on the part of predators). Consequently, the selective pressure from predation will be towards uniformity of colour-pattern across this group of species – hence the difficulty of using colour pattern alone for identification in the field! The coat is also believed to play an important role in regulating body temperature, and it contains many feathery hairs, which are effective in collecting pollen during foraging.

Distribution

The most recent taxonomic study (Williams, 1998) distinguishes 239 species of bumblebee in the world. Unlike many other invertebrate groups, few of these are found in the tropics. Most species are confined to Europe, Asia and America in the Northern Hemisphere, with just a few species in South America and south Asia. Some species have also been successfully introduced into New Zealand and Tasmania.

Some species thrive within the Arctic Circle, and others live at high altitudes in mountainous areas. This ability to survive in environments where air temperatures are often too low for many other insect species is due to the remarkable capacity possessed by bumblebees to regulate their body temperature, maintaining it considerably higher than the surrounding air. As already mentioned, the hairy coat plays a significant role in this. Behaviour also plays a role. Bees can be observed making use of solar energy as they 'sunbathe' whenever conditions allow. They can also uncouple their flight muscles from the wings and generate heat by repeated muscular contractions ('shivering'). In flight, the normal contractions of the wing muscles are only 20-40% efficient, so flight itself generates heat in the body. In addition to these mechanisms of temperature control, bumblebees can make use of a biochemical process, called substrate cycling, which also releases energy (see Heinrich, 1979; Prŷs-Jones, 1986 and Corbet *et al.*, 1993). As well as allowing some species to adapt to high altitudes and northern latitudes, these mechanisms enable bumblebees to forage earlier and later in the day than most other flower-visting insects, thus giving them an advantage over competitors for pollen and nectar. However, on hot summer days bumblebees can suffer from overheating and can often be seen 'grounded'.

Unlike honeybees, bumblebees generally have an annual (or shorter) reproductive cycle, in which only fertilised queens survive the winter period. This adaptation to regular seasonal fluctuations in opportunities for foraging, together with the above capacities for regulating their body temperature, means that bumblebees are 'relatively cold-adapted insects' (Williams, 1989), so that the group as a whole is well within its latitudinal range in Britain.

Most authors include 25 species on the British list (see Table 3.1). However, two of these (*B. cullumanus* and *B. pomorum*) have not been recorded for many years, and the latter may never have been fully established as British species (Alford, 1975).

Williams, in a series of important articles (1982, 1986, 1988, 1989a and 1989b), has analysed national and local distribution patterns for the British species, and tested several rival hypotheses advanced to explain them. Comparing British with Alpine and Scandinavian distributions, he was able to divide the British species into three groups (Williams, 1982). The first of these, the 'Mainland Ubiquitous' species are found throughout mainland Britain (though some of these do have a more southerly distribution than others). This group comprises *B. pascuorum, B. lucorum,*

Table 3.1 The status of bumblebees in the UK and Essex

Species	UK Distribution and Status	Essex Distribution and Status
B. soroeensis	Widespread but local	No confirmed records
B. lucorum	Widespread and common	Widespread and common
B. magnus	Local, mainly northern and western distribution	No records
B. terrestris	Widespread and common in England and Wales	Widespread and common
B. cullumanus	Presumed extinct	No records
B. jonellus	Widespread but local	One confirmed record
B. monticola	Local, but widespread in north and west	No confirmed records
B. pratorum	Widespread and common	Widespread and common
B. lapidarius	Widespread and common throughout	Widespread and common
B. hortorum	Widespread and common	Widespread and common
B. ruderatus	Southern, scarce, and declining. BAP species	Very scarce
B. humilis	Southern, scarce and declining. BAP species	Local, south Essex only
B. muscorum	Local but widespread eastern coastal only	Very local (and declining?)
B. pascuorum	Widespread and common	Widespread and common
B. ruderarius	Local and southern. Declining	Widespread but local. Probably declining.
B. sylvarum	Southern and very scarce. Declining. BAP priority species	Very scarce, south Essex only.
B. distinguendus	Very rare, probably now only in Scottish islands and nearby mainland	No confirmed records
B. subterraneus	Probably extinct	Probably extinct. Was very rare
B. pomorum	Extinct, possibly never established in the UK	No records
B. (P.) bohemicus	Local but widespread. Mainly in north and west	No confirmed records
B. (P.) vestalis	Widespread in south	Widespread and common
B. (P.) rupestris	Was rare but now increasing	Very scarce
B. (P.) barbutellus	Widespread but local	Widespread but local
B. (P.) campstris	Widespread but local in England and Wales	Local
B. (P.) sylvestris	Widespread but local	Widespread but local

B. terrestris, *B. pratorum*, *B. hortorum* and *B. lapidarius*. The second group are the 'Widespread Local Species', which are more thinly distributed, and tend to be more frequent in the north and west. These species are more strongly represented in Arctic Scandinavia and at higher altitudes further south in Europe. Included in this group are *B. muscorum*, *B. monticola*, *B. soroeensis* and *B. jonellus*. The third group are the 'Southern Local' species. These species reach their northern limit within Britain. They include *B. ruderarius*, *B. sylvarum*, *B. humilis*, *B. subterraneus* and *B. ruderatus*. The parasitic species do not fit easily into these divisions, as their distribution is clearly dependent on (but probably is not fully determined by) the distribution and abundance of their respective host species.

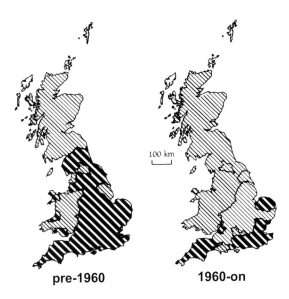

pre-1960   **1960-on**

Fig. 4.1 Pre-1960 and 1960-onwards distributions of true bumblebee species in Britain.

'Mainland Ubiquitous' category shown by broad and narrow diagonal lines

'Local and southern' category shown by broad diagonal lines

'Local but widespread' category shown as grey shading

Redrawn from Williams (1982)

Bumblebee decline

Comparison of the 'pre-1960' and '1960 onwards' distributions of bumblebee species, as presented in the IBRA/ITE *Atlas* (1980), reveals a differentiated pattern of decline among the three groups. 'Mainland Ubiquitous' species remain so since 1960 (though actual population densities may have declined). 'Local but Widespread' species have tended to retreat northwards and westwards, whilst 'Local and Southern' species have retreated, in some cases sharply so, to the south. This leaves an area of central Britain (what Williams calls the 'Central Impoverished Region') more-or-less devoid of all but the ubiquitous species. This is supported by anecdotal evidence from a few relatively well documented localities (see Williams, 1986, 1989).

Clearly, whatever the environmental changes that have been responsible for the alarming decline in many bumblebee distributions, they have not had uniform effects on all species. How can this be explained? Williams has tested three hypotheses, using quantitative analysis of more detailed and fine-grained data from local studies in Kent to complement the larger-scale changes evidenced in the ITE surveys. Drawing on surveys both of bumblebee and floral distributions in Kent, as well as his own systematic comparative study of two sites (Dungeness and Shoreham) he was able to make a number of provisional generalisations:

1. Sites with the ubiquitous species only and those with local species were sharply differentiated. In Kent, sites with shingle, sand dune, saltmarsh, heath, old meadow and undisturbed hedgerows were strongly associated with the presence of the local species.

2.   Sites which supported any local species were likely to support others.

3.   Ubiquitous species tended to be more abundant at sites which also supported the local species.

4.   Where they occur at all, the local species are usually less abundant than the ubiquitous species.

Williams considered the possibility that the patchy distribution of the local species might be due to specialisation on particular plant species as preferred forage sources. Comparing floral distributions with those of local *Bombus* species in Kent did not support this hypothesis. An interesting variant of this hypothesis is that the local species appear to rely on fewer species of forage-plants than the more abundant, ubiquitous species (this is certainly true of the Essex species). Williams argues that this may be partly a consequence of their localisation to very specific habitats, rather than a cause of it. The pattern could also be an artefact of the smaller sample size in the case of the more rarely observed local species. The next possibility was that floristic diversity might be the key factor, in reducing competition between bees of different species at the same site. Again, the evidence did not support this hypothesis. Dungeness (the highest diversity site for bumblebees) was, in fact, less floristically diverse than Shoreham (sustaining only the ubiquitous species (Williams, 1989a and 1989b)).

Williams's own explanation derives from his application of a 'marginal mosaic' model to bumblebees. According to this model, each species of bumblebee is physiologically adapted to a particular climatic and therefore geographical/ latitudinal range. Close to the edge of its range, individuals of a species function less well physiologically than they do closer to the centre. Assuming that foraging efficiency of workers (especially during the period in which the sexual cohort is being reared in the nest) is critical to the reproductive success of the population in a locality, only the most favourable foraging conditions will be tolerated for a species at the edge of its climatic/geographical range. For species nearer the centre of their distributional range, less favourable foraging conditions can be tolerated, though, of course, they will still tend to be more successful at localities which provide the best conditions.

This model fits the observed patterns very well. The local species are close to their latitudinal limits in Britain, and carry energy costs (*e.g.* of thermal regulation) that can only be covered at localities which provide optimal foraging conditions: hence their confinement to a small number of very distinctive localities. Such localities seem to be favourable to (more-or-less) all species, which indicates that competition between species is not the most important factor limiting the number of species in a locality.

This leaves open the question as to what characteristics a locality must possess to provide optimal foraging. Evidence suggests that flowers with longer corolla tubes are more rewarding in terms of nectar provided per visit, and that bees forage with greatest efficiency (other things being equal) from flowers whose corolla tubes are equal to their tongue-length. Williams's comparative study showed that the distribution of tongue and corolla lengths corresponded at Dungeness, but did not at Shoreham, with the consequence that bees at the latter locality had to forage suboptimally on less rewarding flowers with relatively short corolla tubes (Williams, 1989a).

These findings tend to support the 'abundance' hypothesis: that is, that the key factors making for bumblebee diversity in a locality are climate and sheer abundance of the more profitable forage-plants (Williams, 1989a and 1989b). Since one of the most significant energy costs involved in foraging is that incurred by flights between the nest and the forage-plants, density and closeness of suitable forage plants to nest sites will also affect the profitability of workers' foraging activity.

This model of the factors affecting the distribution, localisation and extinction of species does give insights into the causes of the varied patterns of bumblebee decline in Britain over recent decades. Williams considers that climatic cooling up to 1980 could have played some role in the retreat of the 'Southern Local' species. However, this would not explain the retreat in the opposite direction on the part of the 'Widespread Local' species. Williams considers the possibility that urbanisation may be an important factor in destroying good bumblebee habitat. However, though this may be significant, it is unlikely to have produced effects at the level of vice-counties (the units Williams used to display the UK-wide shifts in distributions). More probable as the key factor is agricultural intensification and mechanisation. The extent of conversion to arable farming has been greatest in the midlands. Where arable farming was already more common, in the eastern counties, it has become more intensive, involving hedgerow removal and increases in field sizes associated with mechanisation. Economic pressures have also led to the bringing into cultivation of marginal land. All of these changes are likely to have reduced and fragmented habitats with abundance of the most rewarding food-plants of bumblebees, and have been particularly severe in the 'Central Impoverished Region' of lowland Britain. These changes in land-management may account for widespread local extinction of the local species, and their persistence only in remaining areas of particularly favourable habitat away from their climatic/geographical limit. Williams supplements his argument with evidence of similar patterns of decline elsewhere in Europe (Williams, 1989a).

Powerful as this argument is, there are further questions raised by it. One key assumption is that efficiency of workers in nectar collection is a critical factor affecting the survival or extinction of a population of a species at any site. This factor has the advantages for the researcher that foraging for nectar is an easily observed activity, and that costs and benefits can be measured relatively straightforwardly and subjected to quantitative analysis. However, identifying the flowers that are important for pollen collection, and measuring pollen-collecting efficiency is much more difficult although it could well be an important limiting factor in the success of nest-colonies. It also seems possible that other 'partial habitats' (Westrich, 1990) than foraging habitats may play an important role. These include the presence of sufficient numbers of suitable nest-sites, and nesting materials (especially for the carder bees), suitable hibernation sites, and habitat features required for mate-location behaviours and mating. Diseases, parasitism and predation may also be relevant to varying extents, depending on the species. Since many species use abandoned small mammal nests, but also suffer predation from some mammal species, it would be interesting to research the relationships between the abundance and mix of mammal species in a locality and the bumblebee fauna.

However, it seems most likely that studies of bumblebee distributions which took into account these other aspects of bumblebee ecology would confirm the main point of Williams's argument: that the spread of cultivation together with agricultural industrialisation are the most important causes of observed patterns of bumblebee decline. The changes wrought by these processes have eliminated suitable nesting and hibernation sites, as well as small mammal habitat and flower-rich forage-habitat over a massive swathe of lowland Britain.

Of course, it does not follow that current and future threats to remaining populations of the local and scarce species have to do with agricultural change. Various publicly funded agri-environmental schemes, as well as pressures from consumer groups and environmental social movements could, indeed, contribute to making the farmed countryside marginally more favourable to bumblebees and other wildlife in the future. But irrespective of such issues affecting the wider countryside, it seems likely that significant assemblages of scarce and local species survive today only on sites which for one reason or another have escaped the ravages of industrialised farming. These include large military training areas, nature reserves and country parks, public open spaces and so-called 'brown-field' sites in ex-industrial locations. Such sites are now vulnerable to urban 'development' pressures for new housing and commercial activities in some cases, and to insensitive management regimes in others. It is therefore an urgent responsibility to spread public understanding of the great value of such under-appreciated urban reservoirs of wildlife diversity.

Introduction

Bumblebees are dependent for their food entirely on nectar and pollen, which they obtain from foraging on wild or cultivated flowering plants. The social species establish nests in which at first infertile workers are produced. Eventually these rear a cohort of fertile male and female bees, which mate in the summer or autumn. The males and workers die off before winter sets in and only the fertilised females (queens) survive the winter, to begin the cycle again the following spring. One group, members of the sub-genus *Psithyrus*, is variously described as cuckoos, inquilines or social parasites in the nests of the social species. For simplicity they will be referred to as parasitic or, colloquially, as 'cuckoo' species in this book, though the strict accuracy of this description is questionable. Female *Psithyrus*, or cuckoo bumblebees enter nests already established by one or other of the social species, and lay their eggs there. The workers of the host nest rear the resulting larvae. Since there is no worker caste in the case of the cuckoo bumblebees, these all give rise to either male or female adults. As with the social bumblebees, only the females survive the winter. As well as being subject to 'invasions' by cuckoo bumblebees, nests are also 'home' to a great variety of invertebrates including mites, nematode worms, flies and even moth species. Some of these are internal parasites in the immature stages of the bumblebees, some raid their food-stores, while others are merely scavengers and may even provide benefits for the bumblebees. Owing to their capacity to sting and bite, bumblebees have relatively few predators. Birds sometimes take them and small mammals reputedly attack nests, as also do badgers (S.A. Corbet, pers. com.).

The bumblebee life-cycle

Since much that is of interest in the life-cycle of bumblebees happens inside the nest, there is a limit to what field-observers can discover without intervening in the life of the nest. Close observation, mark-and-release experiments and so on have provided much information, but this has been added to by observing the workings of bumblebee nests in captivity. The great early student of bumblebees, F.W.L. Sladen, was a pioneer in 'domestication' of bumblebees (or 'humble-bees', as he called them) in the latter part of the 19th century, and subsequent researchers have learned much by developing his methods (see especially, Free & Butler, 1959; and Prŷs-Jones & Corbet, 1991).

Bumblebee queens emerge from their hibernation sites in the spring. This may be in February, or even earlier, or as late as April or May, depending on the species and on weather conditions. After hibernation, the internal fat store is almost exhausted, and the ovaries are thread-like and undeveloped. In the days, or weeks, after emergence the queens spend much of their time sunbathing when the opportunity arises and collecting nectar and pollen for their own nutrition. Access to suitable early-flowering forage-plants is very important at this stage, and mortality rates are very high. At night or in inclement weather the bees retreat to shelter (possibly even to former hibernation sites, although this does not seem to have been confirmed) and become torpid.

Soon, however, they introduce another behavioural routine into their daily pattern of activity. They alternate between sunbathing, foraging and prospecting for potential nest-sites. Depending on the species, they closely patrol and explore the contours of tall herbage, banks, ditches, hedge-bottoms, old walls, scrub-margins, riverbanks, compost heaps and old buildings. Occasionally they drop to the ground and disappear for minutes at a time, investigating bare earth among nettle beds, or mossy ground-cover among grass stems. All species show some variability in their preferred nest-sites, but there are definite preferences associated with the different species (see Free & Butler, 1959; Alford, 1975 and Fussell & Corbet, 1993). Several species typically nest underground, usually in a chamber approached by a more-or-less elongated entrance tunnel leading from the surface of the ground. This group includes *B. terrestris*, *B. lucorum*, *B. lapidarius* and probably *B. ruderatus*. They frequently make use of the abandoned nests of small mammals, and their prospecting for nest-sites involves special attention to holes in the ground, which they enter and explore. *B. lapidarius* tends to use holes in bare earth, or adjacent to stones or concrete which may play a role as heat-stores in the temperature regulation of the nests.

Other species, such as *B. pratorum*, *B. jonellus* and *B. pascuorum* are more variable in their selection of sites. This is especially true of *B. pratorum*, which often nests in over-grown gardens, and has been known to use old bird's nests, nest-boxes or tree-roots. A group of species, known collectively as the carder bees, generally nest at or just below the surface of the ground. Like other species, they often make use of disused bird or small mammal nests, but they are also capable of making or modifying their nests by collecting nest materials such as moss, grasses, leaves and fine roots which are then woven into the structure. Later in the year such nests may be extended by the co-operation of chains of workers passing materials back to the nest (see Shuckard, 1866). *Bombus pascuorum* is the most common of the carder bees, but the group also includes some of our most localised and declining species such as *B. humilis* and *B. sylvarum*.

It may take several weeks for a suitable nest-site to be discovered and established. There is evidence of competition between queens of the same or different species for occupancy of particular nest-sites. These sometimes have the dead bodies of previous occupants or failed usurpers around them. It is speculated that queens may invade already-established nests as a way of reducing the costs of establishing nests of their own (Prŷs-Jones & Corbet, 1991). Once established in a potential nest-site, the queen lines it with fine material, and forms a brood-chamber with wax extruded from her abdomen. In some species ('pollen-primers') this is primed with a mass of pollen. The queen also builds a wax cylinder, which she fills with nectar, before laying her first batch of eggs (usually between eight and twelve in number). During this period she spends less time outside the nest on foraging trips (in some years there is a noticeable lull in observable bumblebee activity between the initial period of foraging after hibernation, and the appearance of the first cohort of workers). The brood-chamber is usually given a waxen cover, and the queen incubates the eggs. By spreading her body over the brood-chamber she is able to maintain the temperature well above that of the surrounding environment. The first group of larvae are fed and tended by the queen herself, and during this period queens may be observed with full pollen loads.

The larvae are legless and maggot-like, and shed their skin several times during their development. When fully grown they spin a cocoon, into which they deposit accumulated waste products before pupating. In one or two weeks the adult worker emerges from the cocoon by biting its way out, and/or being helped out by the queen or (later in the life of the colony) other workers. In a few hours to a day, its wings harden and it acquires the full coloration of the coat.

From Sladen's work (1912) it was known that the British species have two rather different feeding regimes for their larvae. He distinguished the 'pocket-makers' and the 'pollen-storers'. The former group includes *B. hortorum* and *B. pascuorum* together with the other carder bees. In these species, pollen is delivered to the larvae in pockets or pouches adjacent to their chamber, and the larvae feed from this store. It is argued that there is competition between the larvae for this food-source, and also that those nearest to the pocket tend to do best. A consequence is that there is supposedly much more variation in size between individual workers in these species. The pollen-storers build wax cylinders, often extending an empty pupal cocoon, into which they place their pollen after foraging trips. The larvae in these species are individually fed, either by the queen, or, later, by the workers, with a mixture of nectar and pollen from the store. The larvae themselves spin separate chambers. It is said that the individual workers in this group of species tend to be more uniform in size. The pollen-storers include *B. lapidarius*, *B. lucorum, B. terrestris* and *B. pratorum*.

Once enough workers have been reared to provide for the brood, the queen remains in the nest, laying eggs at an increasing rate as the number of workers continues to grow. Evidence from studies of some species suggests that the queen lays egg-batches in chambers built on old cocoons in numbers closely related to the numbers of available adult workers to feed the resulting larvae (Brian, 1951).

The workers are, effectively, under-developed females. Under some circumstances they may develop their ovaries and lay eggs. These are unfertilised, and so produce only male offspring. However, the dominance of the queen in the nest generally suppresses the development of workers' ovaries, and they perform a variety of tasks including construction and repair of nest-structures, cleaning out debris, feeding larvae and foraging. In some species, which develop large colonies, some workers also have guard-duties. Research suggests that there are general, though flexible, patterns in the division between foraging and 'housework' activities (see Free & Butler, 1959; Free 1959b; Brian, 1954). For periods of a few days at a time individuals will specialise in one task or the other, though this may have to do with age, as most 'house' bees go on to become foragers later in their lives. Larger workers tend to start foraging earlier in the lives, so that the larger individuals at any one time tend to form the majority of foragers. These patterns can vary depending on the requirements of the colony, and it seems likely that they differ from species to species.

At a certain point in the development of a nest-colony a shift takes place from the production of increasing numbers of workers to the production of males and fertile females, or 'young queens'. Generally, nests reach a maximum size, which varies from species to species. This may be as many as three or four hundred workers, as in *B. terrestris* or *B. lucorum*, but is less than one hundred, and probably much fewer in some other species such as *B. sylvarum*. Then the transition to the production of sexual adults takes place.

The mechanism which triggers this has been the subject of long debate and research. Wheeler (1922) argued that as worker numbers grew, the succeeding larvae would be better nourished and so go on to develop as queens (in the case of the offspring from fertilised eggs). However, Sladen (1912) had doubted whether this could be the sole cause. Subsequent work (Brian, 1980) has shown that there is considerable variation between species. In some, the 'simple' species, the queen has no obvious influence on the transition to the production of young queens. In these species, those larvae which go on to become fully developed queens seem to do so because they have been fed more and for longer. There is some evidence (Free & Butler, 1959) that this has to do with an increase in the ratio of workers to larvae, and that this in turn may be brought about by a slowing down in the rate at which the queen lays eggs. *B. pratorum* and possibly *B. hortorum* belong to this group (see Prŷs-Jones & Corbet, 1991).

In 'complex' species (*e.g. B. terrestris* and possibly *B. lapidarius*) the queen plays a more active role, probably using chemical signals (pheromones) to regulate the workers' activity. She is able in this way to delay the production of sexual adults until large populations of workers have been built up. In the complex species there is a greater disparity in size between workers and queens, and they probably tend to have longer life cycles. In neither group of bumblebees is there any evidence of future queens being fed with distinctive food, as is the case with the 'royal jelly' of the honeybees.

Due to parasitism, inclement weather, or paucity of resources, many nests do not reach the stage of maturity at which the sexual adults are produced. Some nests only produce either males or females, but most that succeed in reaching maturity produce both sexes. The males probably have no significant role in the nest, and soon leave it, never to return. Young queens may play some role in the nest, and are said to sometimes forage to provide for remaining larvae. However, since it is generally believed that the sexual adults are the last cohort reared before the colony breaks up, this is confusing. It is possible that young queens seen with pollen loads in the summer have already mated and have started a second brood in the nest in which they were reared, or, more probably, that they have established their own nests elsewhere and are rearing a second brood. More research is clearly needed on this.

After leaving the nest, the males forage only for themselves, and tend to spend the nights in vegetation, or attached to flower-heads. Much of their time is spent in mate-location activities. These vary from species to species (Free & Butler, 1959; Fussell & Corbet, 1992 and Svensson, 1979). In some (*e.g. B. ruderarius*) the males hover round the nest entrances and mate with fresh females as they emerge. In other species males produce distinctive chemical scents (from the labial gland) with which they mark a series of points in a circuit. They then fly in a regular way over this circuit, stopping every so often at a marked location, and leaving off occasionally to visit flowers. It is assumed that the females are drawn to these circuits by the scent and that they are then encountered by patrolling males. Mating is prolonged, and is accomplished by the (usually much smaller) male perched on the dorsal surface of the female's abdomen. I have found no reference to 'courtship' behaviour in recent literature, but the following account by a Victorian entomologist is irresistibly lurid:

> *In their amours, the autumnal females evince considerable coquetry to attract their partners: they place themselves upon some branch in the most fervid sunshine, and here they practise their cajoleries in the vibrations of their wings, and allure them by their attractive postures. The males are simultaneously abroad, and soon perceive them. The seduction is complete, and they pounce upon them with impetuosity, but their brief indulgence terminates in death, for with his abating vigour the female repulses him, and he falls to the ground never to take wing again.* (Shuckard, 1866)

Whether or not there is any resemblance to the truth in this melodrama, it certainly is the case that the males have no other role in the life of the colony than to fertilise the young queens. The latter build up their internal food-store for the winter by foraging for both nectar and pollen before searching out a suitable place for hibernation. This may vary among species, but may be in a crack in a wall, under vegetation, or, more often, buried in a few centimetres depth of soil in a sheltered, north-facing bank. Shuckard (1866) again:

> *Their fruition is the result of the previous autumn's amours...and accordingly, after revelling in a brief honeymoon, they resort, like staid matrons, to a temporary domicile, some cavity just large enough for themselves.*

Hibernation is not triggered by the approach of winter, as the queens of some species go into hibernation in high summer. In the case of some species, such as *B. terrestris* and *B. lucorum* in southern Britain, females are occasionally seen in the depths of winter, and there is some evidence of all-year-round nesting activity.

In some species that have a short life cycle, such as *Bombus pratorum*, there is evidence that the full life cycle may in favourable seasons be completed twice, or even three times (G.R. Else, pers. comm.). There is some evidence that this may be more common than previously thought, and that it applies to more species. There seems to be some circumstantial evidence of double-broods in recent years in Essex in *B. lucorum*, *B. terrestris* and *B. pascuorum*, as well as *B. pratorum* in some years.

Bumblebees and flowers

Since nectar and pollen are the only food-sources utilised by bumblebees, the diversity, abundance and accessibility of flowers throughout their flight-period play a crucial role in the persistence of bumblebee populations. This relationship with flowers has shaped the evolution of the bumblebee species, but since the flowers, too, benefit from the pollination effected by the bees, their evolution has also been affected. Flowers adapted for insect pollination are said to be 'entomophilous'. Those pollinated by bees show a characteristic 'pollination syndrome': conspicuous colours and scents, bilateral rather than radial symmetry ('zygomorphism'), and secretion of nectar, often protected in a tube or spur. This coevolution between foragers and flowers takes many forms – indeed is not confined to bees, or even to insects. In the tropics, many species of hummingbirds feed exclusively from flowers. In some cases coevolution is so strong that pollination is effected by one bird species only, and that bird can access the nectaries of that one flower only: length and shape of beak and corolla-tube are generally the limiting factor.

In this country, many flowers are pollinated by a range of insects, including butterflies and moths, flies (especially hoverflies (Syrphidae)), and beetles in addition to many bee species, both solitary and social. These visitors to flowers vary greatly in their degree of specialisation to particular groups of flowers, and this may also vary according to whether the insects concerned are foraging for nectar or pollen. Specialist pollen-collectors are said to be 'oligolectic' (Müller, 1996), an evolutionary strategy that may have the effect of increasing efficiency of foraging, or reducing inter-specific competition. Our bumblebees are all generalists (polylectic), but there are observable differences in the foraging 'preferences' of the different species. Long-tongued species tend to forage from flowers with long corolla-tubes (such as the Lamiaceae and Fabaceae), for example, but most will also visit a wide range of other flower species if they are available.

We can distinguish several aspects of the relationship between foraging bumblebees and their food-sources. One such aspect is the caste of the bee, and the stage of development of the colony. After hibernation, queens need ample supplies of pollen and nectar to maintain their activity in seeking out nest sites and establishing their broods and, crucially, to enable development of their ovaries. Until the first cohort of workers can take over, she also forages both for her own nutrition and for the developing larvae. Workers forage to meet their own nutritional requirements as well as those of the successive cohorts of larvae in the nest and the non-foraging 'house-bees', so they must forage efficiently enough to provide a surplus for the colony over and above their own consumption. Males do not take any part in brood rearing, and so their foraging is solely for their own consumption. They forage less persistently and less actively than do workers, and they often visit a different range of forage-sources. Young queens, prior to hibernation, probably play little or no part in the economy of the nest from which they emerge, and their foraging activity is confined to building up their internal food-store (the fat body) to carry them through the winter.

Other aspects of the bee/flower relationship

1.   **Orientation:** bees need to be able to find food-sources, and flowers have evolved ways of enabling them to do so. The bright colours of flowers, as well as, in many cases, their shape appeal to the visual sense of the bees. But bees are highly sensitive to smell, so scent also plays an important part. Having been attracted to the flower the bee still has to locate the nectar and pollen within it, and the flower is also generally structured to maximise the likelihood of the bee brushing pollen from its anthers. It is thought that flower shape, and the presence in many species of lines of marks 'pointing' to the nectaries help to guide the bee, and there is evidence that learning on the part of the bees themselves plays a significant part.

2.   **Access:** bumblebees are large and heavy, compared with most other visitors to flowers. For successful foraging and pollination they need to be provided with a stable platform, or other support, to cling onto. In many cases the shape of the corolla or corolla tube provides this. Flowers with long corolla tubes or 'spurs' containing nectar may not be accessed by many species, so that the 'assemblage' of pollinating insects will be restricted to those with long tongues or other adaptations. However, some of the shorter-tongued species bite holes at the base of the corolla-tubes of some flower species and 'rob' them of their nectar without brushing against the anthers. Other insects, such as honeybees (*Apis mellifera*), often subsequently use these holes, as 'secondary robbers'. Pollen collecting can also be achieved by 'buzz-foraging'. Bees alight on a flower and vibrate their thorax at a frequency which triggers an explosive release of pollen (Corbet *et al.*, 1988; King, 1993). In some flowers, notably snapdragons, the corolla-tube is closed at the apex, and has to be forced open if the forager is to reach pollen or nectar. Only large and powerful insects such as bumblebees are able to forage from such flowers.

3   **Reward:** Flowers vary considerably in the amount of nectar they secrete, in the ease of access to it, and in the pattern of secretion through the day. These are

important variables, which affect the pattern of foraging behaviour by the different castes and species of bumblebee. A very interesting study carried out in Cambridge Botanic Gardens compared the rates and timing of nectar-secretion of ten species of wild flowers, and observed the patterns of insect visits through the day (Comba, Corbet, Hunt, & Warren, 1999). Massed flowers, yellow Fabaceae, and mallows were attractive to *B. lapidarius*. *B. hortorum*, a long-tongued species, was not observed to have a different pattern of foraging from the short-tongued species in this study, though it is known to visit such deep flowers as red campion and foxglove. Marsh and hedge woundworts were visited frequently by *B. pascuorum* and also by a solitary bee, *Anthidium manicatum*. The males of this latter species are territorial, and dart towards insects encroaching on their local patch of woundwort. Observations showed a pattern of early visits by *B. pascuorum,* which benefited from high standing crops of nectar at this time of day. *Anthidium* was observed mainly in the middle part of the day, with a return of *B. pascuorum* towards evening. It is possible that *B. pascuorum* was discouraged from foraging from these plants in the middle of the day by being dashed at by the solitary bee, whilst the latter appeared to be limited in the timing of its visits by its higher temperature threshold than that of *B. pascuorum*. Teasel was shown to secrete very small quantities of nectar per flower, but was frequently visited by several *Bombus* and *Psithyrus* species. The density of flowers in a single head (capitulum) presumably compensates for the low yield per flower by requiring less energy expenditure in moving from flower to flower.

As the authors point out, their study was limited in its general significance by several features of such studies. The frequency of visits by insects to a particular flower or plot will depend very much on the local availability of alternative forage sources, and also the species noted will be limited by the local pool and abundance of pollinating insect species. Lack of visits to a particular flower species in such a study therefore cannot be taken to imply lack of value as a forage source at other times or places. However, frequency of visits *can* justify the conclusion that a given species of flower may be a valuable food source. It might also be noted that field identification by colour pattern limits the relevance of the study to common and readily identified species. The timing of the observations (July and August) is such that workers, queens and males of several species would have been included in the study. Different foraging patterns by sex and caste seem likely, and would not have been noted. Finally, the authors focussed on foraging for nectar, as this is more easily measured. However, it seems likely that bumblebees are dependent upon a much narrower range of forage plants for their pollen requirements. Observational studies of pollen collection and analysis of pollen-loads is a very illuminating avenue for further research (on pollen analysis see Moore & Webb, 1978 and Westrich, 1999).

An earlier national survey, carried out by members of WATCH and the London Wildlife Trust under the direction of Fussell and Corbet (see Fussell & Corbet 1992b and 1993), used relatively inexperienced observers in an attempt to assess the value of a very wide range of wild and cultivated forage sources for bumblebees. Bee identification was based on colour-groupings, as above, and participants were asked to report on flower visits by bumblebees on regular walks. Notwithstanding the unavoidable limitations of such a survey, interesting results were obtained. One very striking result was the sheer range and variety of flowering plants reported. Plants reported as visited by bumblebees five or more times totalled more than 280 taxa. Since many plants were not identified down to species level, the number of species visited may well have been significantly higher than this. The findings of complementary studies on a local basis were largely confirmed, with characteristic differentiation between the forage preferences of long- and short-tongued species, and the 'popularity' of some groups of flowers, such as Lamiaceae (especially deadnettles), Fabaceae (vetches and clovers), and Asteraceae, plus individual species such as bluebell, teasel, honeysuckle, comfrey, bramble, and foxglove.

However, perhaps the greatest value of the survey (apart from the benefit of engaging the interest and involvement of large numbers of lay observers) was in its revelation of the diversity of cultivated flowers extensively used by foraging bumblebees (see below). Since gardens are private space, it is not easy for individual researchers to do comprehensive surveys without alarming householders, or themselves becoming objects of suspicious observation!

Worker bumblebees do not appear to have any equivalent of the honeybee's 'dance' to communicate the location of good forage sources, but they do move from species to species of plant in accord with peak flowering periods. Heinrich (1976) has shown that foraging bumblebees become more efficient with learning. In addition, mark-and-release studies show a high degree of patch-fidelity on the part of individual foragers, which return to the same patch and follow a regular route through it.

4.   **Pollination:** Plant species may benefit in various ways from insect pollination. Some species (such as clovers) are not self-fertile, and so depend for seed-set on insect pollinators. Other plant species produce higher quality seed or fruit, or more vigorous subsequent generations, or simply more seeds if pollinated by insects. Yet other species (such as oil-seed rape) are self-pollinating but benefit from the mechanical action of insects in knocking pollen from anthers to stigma.

Bumblebees are particularly efficient pollinators of both wild and cultivated flower species. Since workers are foraging not just for themselves but for larvae in the nest, each individual makes more visits than do many 'solitary' species. The hairy coat collects pollen, the longer tongues than many other insects give them access to a wider range of flower shapes and sizes, and their capacity to raise their body temperature enables them to forage earlier and later in the day, in more inclement weather, and also earlier in the spring.

As we saw above, some species of bumblebee (notably *B. terrestris*, but also *B. lucorum*) are capable of robbing flowers of their nectar without pollinating them. The technique of buzz-foraging may also reduce pollination in the short-tongued species of bumblebee, which often do not probe the corolla tube for nectar (see King, 1993). However, buzz-foraging may trigger pollination in some flower species. As Corbet, Williams & Osborne (1991) point out, the conservation of many rare and endangered wild plant species in Europe may be dependent on insect pollination, but, probably because of limited economic interest, there has so far been too little research on this.

Effectiveness of insects as pollinators must depend significantly on the constancy of individual foragers to flowers of a single species. Since bumblebees are generalists in their foraging behaviour, the extent of this constancy over time is of considerable interest. Studies of pollen loads (see Free & Butler, 1959; Free, 1970a and Prŷs-Jones & Corbet, 1991) suggest that though approximately half of them contain pollen from more than one plant species, the majority of mixed loads are predominantly composed of pollen from one species. This suggests a high degree of constancy, presumably maximising the benefits of experience and learning on the part of the foraging bee, and also increasing its value as a pollinator.

Bumblebees and cultivated plants

This relationship can be considered from two points of view. As already noted, bumblebees have a significant role in pollination of many horticultural and agricultural crops. The decline in populations of many – perhaps all – bumblebee species can be viewed from the standpoint of the potential loss of their service as effective pollinators, and the sorts of land-management strategies which might halt or even reverse recent trends. The alternative point of view starts from a concern with bumblebee conservation, and explores ways in which gardens, orchards, farms and other forms of cultivation can be managed to enhance bumblebee habitat. Of course, there will be a large overlap (the larger the better) in the practical implications of both sorts of concern.

Corbet, Williams & Osborne (1991) list over 40 major crop plants in the EU which benefit from bee pollination. This list does not include the many Mediterranean herbs and spices for which no statistics were available, and nor does it include the increasing use of bumblebees for pollination of glasshouse crops such as tomatoes, and in hybrid seed production. For reasons given above, bumblebees are particularly effective pollinators, and their potential economic significance has increased with the loss of honeybees to the *Varroa jacobsoni* mite. However, there are relatively few experimental studies of the effect of bumblebee pollination on particular crop yields. Studies have demonstrated its value for the field bean in the UK (Free & Williams, 1976; Stoddard & Bond, 1987, and see references in Corbet, Williams & Osborne, 1991), and Macfarlane *et al.* (1983) discovered dramatically increased seed set in red clover as a result of augmenting bumblebee populations in New Zealand (see also Free, 1970b and McGregor, 1976). A study carried out on Cambridge University's farm (Fussell & Corbet, 1991) showed the long-tongued bumblebees *B. hortorum* and *B. pascuorum* to be significant pollinators of field bean. Shorter-tongued bumblebees and honeybees also visited field bean and oil-seed rape, but (in the case of field beans) either robbed them, without brushing against the anthers, or visited nectaries on the stipules. The authors point out that these crops provide nutrition for the bees for a relatively short period only. If their pollinating services are to be provided, then there must be both nesting sites nearby and a continuous succession of alternative forage-sources through the spring and summer.

This requires provision and appropriate management of suitable semi-natural habitat within the agricultural landscape. The most visited forage sources by *B. pascuorum* and *B. hortorum* were white dead-nettle, black horehound, hedge woundwort, bramble, creeping and spear thistles. The shorter-tongued species also favoured black horehound, bramble and creeping thistle, together with hogweed. Another 26 plant taxa are listed as less frequently visited.

Fussell and Corbet argue the importance of retaining areas of permanent grassland, on track or road verges, field boundaries, hedge-banks, and other marginal land. Bumblebees depend on the more nectar-rich perennial and biennial wild flowers (though some annuals, such as red dead-nettle, and common hempnettle are also rich in nectar). Since perennials may take several years to become established these areas must be left uncultivated, with infrequent grazing or cutting to prevent scrub encroachment. Corbet, Saville & Osborne (1994) add farm woodland, if appropriately managed, as valuable bumblebee habitat (though Williams (1988) showed the inside of *closed* woodlands to be poor for bumblebees). Young plantations, woodland edges, and permanent rides provide open areas with undisturbed soil where perennial flowers can become established. Where land is taken out of cultivation, bumblebee habitat can be created by allowing natural regeneration, with the proviso that the annual plants which will flower in the first year will be of relatively little value, and will include weeds of arable cultivation. Alternatives include sowing appropriate wildflower seed mixes, or bee forage-crops. The latter include some unusually nectar-rich annuals such as borage, sunflower and kale.

Corbet (1995) reviewed studies in the USA and Europe on set-aside. Although short-term set-aside is advocated for conservation of some rare arable weeds, and also for insect-food for game birds, there is a strong case for longer-term set-aside. Succession studies show that if land is not ploughed or treated with herbicide after the first year, a sward of perennial plants becomes established and progressively suppresses annual weeds. There are associated benefits for both agriculture and conservation. Increasing diversity of perennials with length of time since cultivation allows the establishment of rarer and declining species. Stature of vegetation increases, along with architectural and microclimatic diversity. These features increase the entomological diversity of the plot and, in particular, provide nesting sites, larval host-plants, and forage sources for larger pollinating insects such as butterflies and bumblebees. As succession proceeds beyond the third year, set-aside affords benefits in the form of crop-pollination and natural pest control for adjacent agricultural land. In the longer term, some management is required to suppress scrub-development and the shading out of herbaceous plants. Corbet suggests that bumblebees may be regarded as 'keystone' species, in the sense that they are particularly important to the persistence of ecological communities by virtue of their role in pollination. For this reason, measures to protect common but declining bumblebee species may have more conservation value than attempts to 'save' particular rarities, which have few ecological interdependencies.

The ability of bumblebees to sustain populations in agricultural landscapes will depend to some extent on how widely dispersed their semi-natural and crop forage sites are. The high energy costs of flights between nests and forage sites mean that optimal foraging conditions, other things being equal, will involve rich forage-sites close to nesting sites. There are relatively few studies of the distances travelled by bumblebees, but such evidence as there is suggests that they may fly considerably further than might be expected on the basis of assumptions about energy efficiency. A study carried out on an arable landscape in south eastern Norway (Saville *et al.*, 1997), involving both mark-and-release and dawn-to-dusk observation at a nest of *B. lucorum*, revealed that though bees marked while foraging showed a high degree of fidelity to particular patches, those marked at the nest were relatively rarely re-observed at monitored forage sites within 250 metres of the nest. This suggested that the main forage-patches being used by these bees were outside the study-area, and more than 250 m from the nest. Subsequent work using sophisticated tracking methods have revealed that workers can return to their nests quickly from several kilometres away, and that distances of more than five hundred meters between foraging sites and nests are frequent in *B. terrestris* (Osborne *et al.*, 1999). This knowledge is currently of considerable interest, given the controversy over the effectiveness of buffer zones round so-called 'experimental' genetically modified crops.

As agricultural practices have become increasingly inhospitable to bumblebees, it seems likely that gardens have become more important as refuges for foraging workers and queens. The national survey conducted by Fussell & Corbet (1992b and 1993) was particularly valuable in drawing attention to the extent of this, and to the wide variety of garden plants visited by bumblebees. Their list of plant taxa reported as visited more than five times by bumblebees includes no fewer than 48 garden shrubs and trees, and 107 garden flowers. Early flowering shrubs such as *Ribes sanguineum*, *Berberis* and fruit trees and shrubs were frequently visited. Later in the year, *Rhododendron*, *Lavandula*, *Calluna* and *Erica* spp., *Buddleia* and *Symphoricarpus*, were frequented by 'banded red tails' (mainly *B. pratorum*, presumably) and *Cotoneaster horizontalis* was particularly popular with all species. Among the herbaceous taxa, *Pentaglottis, Aruncus, Limnanthes, Lupinus* and *Campanula* are particularly noted for the short-tongued species, and *Consolida* (larkspur), *Nepeta, Salvia, Digitalis, Aconitum, Symphytum, Origanum, Centaurea* and *Impatiens* for the longer-tongued species.

The value of gardens as forage-habitat poses the question of the relative value to bees of different 'cultivars'. A study by Comba, Corbet, Barron *et al.* (1999) investigated the effects of changes in floral structure, size and nectar secretion on bumblebee foraging for cultivars of *Tropaeolum majus, Consolida, Antirrhinum majus, Viola* spp. and *Tagetes patula*. In some cases more nectar was secreted by the more transformed cultivars, but alterations in floral structure rendered it less accessible. In some cases the loss of a functional spur, or, in the case of snapdragons, reduction in the obstacles to entry into the corolla tube, changed the assemblage of insects able to access the pollen in favour of shorter-tongued species, including hoverflies (Syrphidae), solitary bees and honeybees. Comba *et al.* recommend planting the more unmodified cultivars of plants such as snapdragon, nasturtium and larkspur.

Deliberate planting of bumblebee-friendly garden shrubs and herbaceous flowers, as well as encouraging wildflowers known to be beneficial, could play an important part in the conservation of our commoner species. It would also reward the gardener with much added interest and wildlife diversity. Much valuable research could be done by observing bumblebee visits to garden flowers to amplify our current stock of knowledge about which species and cultivars are most rewarding. C. Gibson (pers. comm.) reports that *Echium pininana*, a relative of viper's bugloss, is outstandingly attractive to bumblebees. In addition, more needs to be known about the extent to which certain species can utilise gardens for other habitat-requirements such as nesting and hibernating.

Cuckoo bumblebees (subgenus *Psithyrus*)

These used to be assigned to a separate genus (*Psithyrus*) from the 'true' bumblebees (*Bombus*). However, systematic work by Williams (1994) has given convincing reasons for including them in an enlarged single genus *Bombus*. The evidence is that the cuckoo bumblebees all share a common ancestor (they constitute a 'clade'). However, they also share common ancestors with some true bumblebees, which are not shared by other groups of *Bombus*. The upshot is that *Psithyrus* could only be retained as a separate genus at the cost of dividing up the true bumblebees into several different genera. The alternative solution of uniting the cuckoo bumblebees with the social species into an enlarged genus *Bombus* now seems generally accepted.

There are just six species of cuckoo bumblebees in Britain. Each is normally parasitic

Table 4.1 Cuckoo bumblebees and their hosts (data from Løken, 1984)

Cuckoo bumblebee	Usual host bumblebee	Occasional hosts
B. (Psithyrus) vestalis	Bombus terrestris	
B. (Psithyrus) bohemicus	Bombus lucorum	
B. (Psithyrus) barbutellus	Bombus hortorum	
B. (Psithyrus) rupestris	Bombus lapidarius	B. sylvarum and B pascuorum
B. (Psithyus) campestris	Bombus pascuorum	B. humilis and B. pratorum
B. (Psithyrus) sylvestris	Bombus pratorum	B. jonellus
B. (Psithyrus) bohemicus is a predominantly northerly species, and I have no evidence of its occurrence in Essex. The other five species are regularly recorded in the county, though B. (Psithyrus) rupestuis is currently rather rare and localised.		

on a particular host species, although there is evidence that some *Psithyrus* species are less host-specific than was previously thought (Løken, 1984). See Table 4.1 above.

In general terms the life history of the cuckoo bumblebees is well understood, but differences in host/parasite relationships in detail, and in relation to individual species require more research. They are very similar to 'true' bumblebees in appearance, but generally the coat is sparser, and they lack the pollen baskets and associated structures on the hind legs. Since they rely on the workers of the host bumblebee species to nurture their larvae they do not have a worker caste of their own. Neither do female cuckoo bumblebees have the capacity to secrete wax. In some cases, for example *B. (P.) rupestris*, there is a close resemblance in colour pattern between cuckoo and host, but this is less marked in other species, and it seems likely that visual resemblance is not generally important in securing acceptance of invading 'cuckoo' females by host workers.

It is generally asserted that cuckoo females emerge from hibernation later than the host queens, but in some species (notably *B. (P.) vestalis*) they may be observed very early in the spring. After a period of foraging during which their ovaries develop to maturity, they begin prospecting for nests. Their behaviour in this activity resembles that of queen true bumblebees, though, of course, they are searching not for potential nest-sites, but for already-established nests of the host species.

On entry into a nest they may be attacked by host workers, but their thick cuticle is believed to offer protection from the stings of the former. They subsequently hide in nest-materials until they (presumably) acquire the distinctive scent of the nest, and no longer attract the hostility of the host workers. It has been thought that invader–cuckoo females invariably kill the incumbent queen, but it seems that this is not always the case. There is some speculation that *Psithyrus* females which parasitise 'simple' species are more likely to tolerate host queens.

When the host nest has sufficient workers to nurture the larvae of the cuckoo female, she destroys the host eggs and larvae, using the wax/pollen mixture from their cells to make cells for her own eggs. Beyond this she plays no further role in the economy of the nest. The host workers nurture the resulting 'cuckoo' larvae, which subsequently pupate and emerge as male or female adults. Male cuckoo bumblebees generally resemble the females, but are smaller. They patrol regular routes between scent-marked spots, as do male true bumblebees, as their strategy for locating mates (Fussell & Corbet, 1992c). After mating, the females forage to build up their fat bodies, prior to hibernation. Males forage rather sluggishly for their own nutrition only, and eventually die off prior to the onset of winter.

*As mentioned above, the cuckoo bumblebees have a common ancestor, which was presumably a true bumblebee. The parasitic mode of life may have evolved from the commonly observed conflict between queens of the same or different species of true bumblebees for a single nest-site. Sladen (1912) gives an example of a queen *B. terrestris* invading a nest of *B. lucorum* and having the workers of the latter rear its young. Prŷs-Jones & Corbet (1991) also cite true bumblebees in the Arctic or at high altitudes behaving like cuckoos.

Other friends and enemies

The possession by bumblebees of the ability to sting, together with their warning coloration probably protects them to a considerable degree from predation by birds and mammals. However, considerable numbers of nests are believed to be destroyed by field mice and other rodents. Badgers, too, are partial to the contents of bumblebee nests. A discussion of the mystery of dead bumblebees beneath lime trees, at a meeting of the Essex Field Club (Essex Field Club, 1884) yielded the consensus that the bees had become intoxicated by the lime nectar, and rendered vulnerable to attacks by red-backed shrikes. However, despite the current absence of shrikes from Essex, it is still common to find bumblebees of several species with the tip of the abdomen clipped off and the abdominal contents removed. Sometimes there is also a hole in the dorsal surface of the thorax. Since the current culprit is most unlikely to be the shrike, it seems likely that some other bird species – probably one or more species of tits – is a regular predator on bumblebees, and has developed a method of attack that avoids being stung.

Parasites and commensals of bumblebee nests are immensely varied, and constitute an ecological community in their own right. Among the internal parasites the most important are nematode worms (of the species *Sphaerularia bombi*). These are free-living in soil during the summer, but enter the bodies of hibernating female *Bombus* in autumn. In the following spring they lay huge numbers of eggs, and the resulting worms consume the internal organs and fluids of the bee. This is said to be the most important cause of spring mortality in over-wintered queens in some areas. Other parasites of adults and larvae include conopid flies (such as *Conops* spp. and *Sicus* spp.), mites such as *Tarsonemus* spp., a protozoan (*Nosema bombi*), a tachinid fly (*Brachycoma devia*), and the larvae of the bumblebee wax-moth (*Aphomia sociella*). Other commensals may consume some of the food supplies in the nest, but also perform beneficial scavenging functions. These include the larvae of some hoverflies of the genus *Volucella*, and *Antherophagus* beetles. Particularly common and noticeable are tiny mites of the genus *Parasitellus*. These cling to the bodies of newly emerged females, often in the area between head and thorax, and remain attached to them through the winter and until a new nest is established during the following spring. Alford (1975) provides fascinating detail on these associates of bumblebees (see also Macfarlane, Lipa & Liu, 1995).

Introduction

One of the reasons I chose to study bumblebees was that, as a father and full-time worker, I thought I would have only enough spare time to deal with a small group of insects, which would be easy to identify. I soon found out how wrong I was! Certainly, the number of species is small, but the problems only start there.

First, there are several groups of common insects that are very plausible mimics of bumblebees. These include flies, especially certain hoverflies (Syrphidae) and bee-flies (*Bombylius major*), beetles (Coleoptera), certain day-flying moths, especially the bee hawkmoths (*Hemaris* spp.), and some species of solitary bees (notably the black females of *Anthophora plumipes*).

Second, the bumblebees are, as we have seen, conventionally divided into true bumblebees and cuckoo bumblebees (subgenus *Psithyrus*). In the case of the true bumblebees it is necessary to be able to identify males, and females of two castes (workers and queens). In some species, the different sexes and castes are alike, but in others they are not. In the case of cuckoo bumblebees, the two sexes (there is no worker caste) are often different in colour pattern.

Finally, the colour-patterns, which are the most obvious and convenient characteristics to use for field-identification, are subject to quite a lot of individual variation in some species. Sometimes this takes the form of a general darkening of the pattern, with reduction or even loss of pale bands, and, in some species, entirely black specimens. Aged or worn individuals can also be misleadingly faded.

Wherever there is doubt, and where truly definitive identification is required, it is necessary to base identification on structural, anatomical characteristics. Sometimes these can be observed in living specimens, and where possible I have referred to these features in the key below. However, there are some species and castes that cannot be definitively identified without dissection and microscopic examination. Even then it may not be possible to definitively identify some individuals – especially in the case of small workers of closely related species.

Is it a bumblebee?

However effective the mimics are, it is usually quite easy to tell them from the 'real thing' with experience. Some general distinguishing features of bumblebees are given below, but it may be easier simply to learn to identify the more common mimics directly (see chapter 8).

Bumblebees have two pairs of translucent wings, and simple antennae consisting of 12 or 13 segments (fig. 5.6). By contrast, all flies have only one pair of wings, and a variety of differently shaped antennae (fig. 5.1). Beetles (Coleoptera) have two pairs of wings, but the front pair is hardened to form a protective casing under which the hind wings are folded when the insect is not in flight. The only bumblebee mimic beetle (*Emus hirtus*) known from Essex is presumed extinct in the county. Bee hawkmoths are rare in Essex (we have only one species, *H. fuciformis*), and have an outer margin of scales on the wing surfaces. Some species of 'solitary' bee may cause confusion. The most bumblebee-like of these is the black female of the *Anthophora plumipes*, which is widespread in Essex and commonly seen in gardens during the spring, foraging from the same flowers as bumblebees. In the field, the easiest way to distinguish it is by the dense yellow hairs that cover the hind tibiae (see fig. 5.2). These are superficially similar to pollen-baskets laden with yellow pollen, but a closer look dispels the illusion. The males of this species are also quite similar in appearance to bumblebees, with tawny-brown hair on the body. However, they are easily distinguished from all bumblebees by the long hairs sprouting from the foot-segments (tarsi) of the middle pair of legs and a yellow mark on the cuticle of the face.

Is it a 'true' or a 'cuckoo' bumblebee?

Generally, the coat of cuckoo bumblebees is more sparse than that of true bumblebees, and they are said to be more lethargic when foraging. These may be useful tips toward field identification, but they are, of course, not reliable

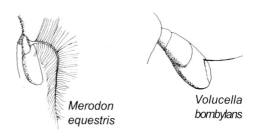

Merodon equestris   *Volucella bombylans*

Fig. 5.1 Antennae of two hoverflies that mimic bumblebees

Fig. 5.2 Hind leg of the bumblebee-mimic *Anthophora plumipes*

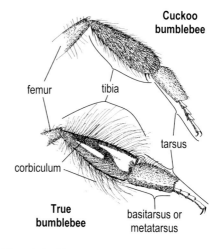

Cuckoo bumblebee

femur   tibia

corbiculum

tarsus

True bumblebee

basitarsus or metatarsus

Fig. 5.3 Hind legs of cuckoo bumblebees (subgenus *Psithyrus*) and true bumblebees

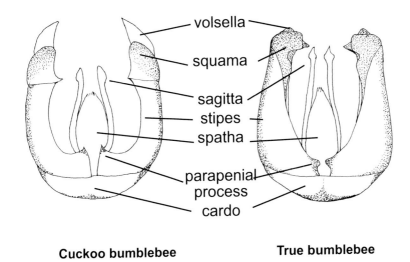

Cuckoo bumblebee   **True bumblebee**

Fig. 5.4 Genital capsules of male cuckoo bumblebees and true bumblebees

guides. The best characteristic for separating true from cuckoo bumblebees is the structure of the hind tibiae. These are flat, or nearly so, and more-or-less shiny, with a fringe of long hairs in both male and female 'true' bumblebees. If there are hairs on the surface (males) they are usually very sparse, and unbranched. In cuckoo bumblebees, the hind tibiae are dull, convex and densely hairy. There is no pollen basket as in the true bumblebees (see fig. 5.3). If dead specimens can be examined, male true bumblebees can be distinguished from cuckoo males by differences in their genital capsule (large, pale volsellae exposed beyond the squamae in subgenus *Psithyrus* (with the exception of *B.(P.) sylvestris)*; variable, but generally small, dark and partially obscured behind the squamae in true bumblebee males, see fig. 5.4). Females can be distinguished by the differently shaped mandibles (more-or-less blunt-ended in true bumblebees, oblique outer margin in subgenus *Psithyrus* females, see fig. 5.5) and by the variously shaped callosities on the ventral surface of the final segment of the abdomen (see fig. 5.33).

Is it a male or a female?

In the field, any bumblebee with a full pollen-load is a female (worker or queen) true bumblebee. In the early spring (from February through to about the middle of May) almost any bumblebee you see will be a female (worker or queen) true bumblebee, or a female cuckoo bumblebee. When first learning to identify bumblebees, it greatly simplifies things if you concentrate your observations at this time of year. Later in the year, males are on the wing, and you need to be able to distinguish the sexes in order to use the complete key.

There are three characteristics that can be used to do this. The first is the number of segments in the antennae – 12 in females, 13 in males (see fig. 5.6). The method of tubing and releasing live specimens can be used to check this, but keeping the bee still enough while you hold a lens to the tube and count the segments is not easy! The second characteristic is that males have seven abdominal segments visible from above, while females have six. Again, this is not easy to determine in live specimens. Thirdly, the hind

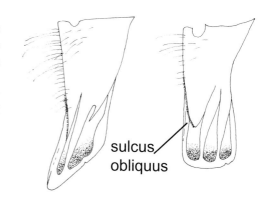

Cuckoo bumblebee   True bumblebee

Fig 5.5 Right mandibles of female true bumblebee and cuckoo bumblebee

end of the abdomen in males is rounded, with a wide slit enclosing the genital capsule. Gentle pressure on the abdomen reveals at least the tip of this. The tip of the female abdomen is pointed and encloses the sting. Sometimes an irritated captive specimen will extend the sting, thus revealing its sex as female. This third feature is generally the easiest to use in 'sexing' bumblebees.

In my own experience it was necessary to spend a couple of seasons learning how to identify the common species of bumblebees with reasonable reliability from field observation. In fact, the vast majority of bumblebees seen in most parts of the county will belong to one or other of six common species of true bumblebees, and four cuckoos. It is helpful to know how to identify these readily, so that the rarer or more localised species can then be picked out as 'something different'. This is what the following introductory guide is designed to do. When you have got as far as this guide allows you to go, then move on to the Key for more critical identification of all species likely to be seen in Essex (and the rest of southern England). As well as these common species, I have included reference in the Introductory Guide to a more localised true bumblebee, and a (currently) rare cuckoo bumblebee. These are fairly easy for the beginner to distinguish (and, in the case of the cuckoo, may be on the increase).

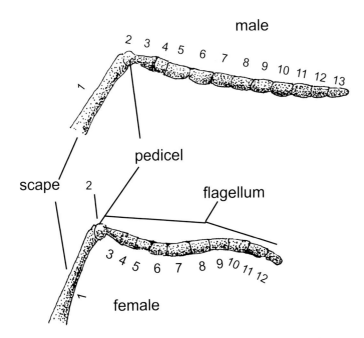

Fig 5.6 Antennae of male and female bumblebees

An identification guide to the common Essex bumblebees.

Notes:

- This guide will not work for all specimens (east coast marshes, and southern strip of Essex have rare or local species not covered).
- This guide will not work for species that do not occur in Essex.
- Some common species have unusual colour forms that are not covered in this guide.
- Old or worn specimens may often be misleading in appearance.
- Check the text above to make sure your specimen is a bumblebee and not a 'mimic'.
- Colour patterns referred to are hair-colours (all bumblebees have black bodies).

The Guide:

Hind tibiae flattened, and with a fringe of long hair (fig. 5.3)   **A**

Hind tibiae convex, with a dense coat of short hair (fig. 5.3)   **B**

A. True Bumblebees

All black, with red tail.

- Pollen-basket with black hairs   ***Bombus lapidarius*** female
- Pollen basket with ginger, or ginger-tipped hairs
                                            Bombus ruderarius female

One yellow band (collar), red tail

- With yellow hairs on the face   ***Bombus lapidarius*** male
- No yellow hairs on face   ***Bombus pratorum*** female

Two yellow bands (collar and abdomen), and red tail. Band 2 (abdomen) may be reduced or missing.

- No yellow hair on face   ***Bombus pratorum*** female
- Both yellow bands present, and wide. Yellow on face
                                            Bombus pratorum male

Three yellow bands (collar, scutellum, abdomen), and white tail. Long face   ***Bombus hortorum***

 (similar to ***B. jonellus*** and the very rare ***B. ruderatus*** – see main key)

Two yellow bands (collar and abdomen),

- Large, with buff tail   ***Bombus terrestris*** queen
- Large or small with white tail   ***Bombus terrestris*** male or
                                                                worker
                                    or ***Bombus lucorum*** (see main key)

Thorax ginger-brown, abdomen with very variable mixture of orange-brown and black hairs

                                            Bombus pascuorum
        (similar to localised ***B. muscorum*** and ***B. humilis*** – see main key)

Fig. 5.7 Colour patterns for the identification of common true bumblebees

B. Cuckoo bumblebees (subgenus *Psithyrus*)

Large, black with red tail. Darkened wings
> **B. (*Psithyrus*) *rupestris*** female (rare in Essex)

One or more indistinct yellow bands, red tail
> **B. (*Psithyrus*) *rupestris*** male (rare in Essex)

One or two yellow bands (collar and sometimes abdomen). White tail with yellow side-flashes.
> **B. (*Psithyrus*) *vestalis***

One or two yellow bands (collar and scutellum), tail yellow
> **B. (*Psithyrus*) *campestris*** male (pale form)

One or two yellow bands (collar and scutellum), tail black with yellow at the sides. Coat on abdomen very thin towards the middle
> **B. (*Psithyrus*) *campestris*** female

One or two yellow bands. Whitish tail (no yellow flashes at sides)
> **B. (*Psithyrus*) *sylvestris***
> or **B. (*Psithyrus*) *barbutellus*** (see main key)
> (also faded specimens of **B. (*P.*) *vestalis***)

Fig. 5.8 Colour patterns for the identification of cuckoo bumblebees

Complete Key to the Bumblebees of Essex

Notes:

- This key is designed to enable identification of all Essex species of *Bombus* (including both true and cuckoo bumblebees).

- Extinct species, and species not so far recorded in Essex, but found elsewhere in southern England, are included.

- Characters which can be observed on living specimens in the field are used as far as possible, but for critical identifications anatomical features, observable only with dissection, may have to be used.

- Some species have entirely black (melanic) colour-forms. In a few cases (the males of two species of true bumblebees, and two species of cuckoo bumblebees) these occur frequently enough to be included in the key. More unusual melanic forms are omitted from the key, but may still be identified by using the anatomical figures and plates.

- For interpretation of the terms used in the key to refer to anatomical features, see figs 5.3, 5.4, 5.5, 5.6, 5.9 and 5.10. Where reference is made to abdominal segments, the dorsal surface is intended unless otherwise specified.

- Suggestions on improving the key will be much appreciated by the author.

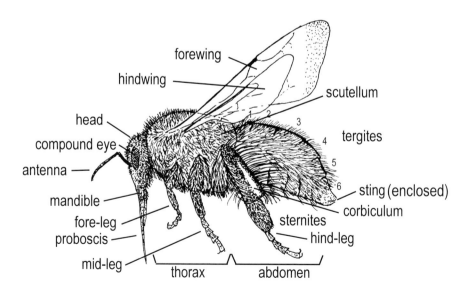

Fig. 5.9 The external features of a female bumblebee

Fig 5.10 Exposed sting-sheath of female bumblebee (ventral posterior view)

Fig. 5.11 Technique for exposing male genital capsule

Techniques

Many anatomical features are can be observed with a hand-lens or microscope without difficulty. However, some features used below concern structures that are normally internal, and require some skill to access. These are features of the male genital capsule, and the sting-sheath in the females of true bumblebees. Generally, the structures of the male genitalia are useful for identification, whilst the sting sheaths of the females are in some cases not very distinctive. Since these features can only be observed in dead specimens, it is in any case better, from the point of view of conservation, to take males (where this has to be done at all).

Male genitalia: Exert pressure on the hind-segments of the abdomen from both ventral and dorsal sides, using a pair of forceps. The capsule 'pops' out, as in fig. 5.11.

Sting-sheath: This is a more difficult operation (figs. 5.12(a-d)). Using a fine-tipped pair of forceps, the sting is pulled out from its enclosure within segment 6 of the abdomen. This involves some tearing of the tissue attaching it to the inner abdomen. At this point, the sting can be bent up and forward, exposing the ventral surface of the structure which holds the sting (fig. 5.12c). This is the 'sting-sheath'. When this is viewed from behind (as in fig. 5.12d) inner flaps or projections can be seen within the arch formed by the two sides of the sheath.

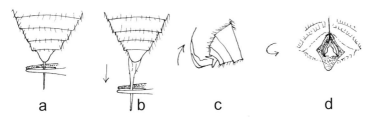

Fig. 5.12 Technique for exposing the sting-sheath of female bumblebees

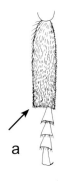

The Key:

1. Hind tibiae flattened, shiny, and with fringe of long hairs (corbiculum). (If hairs on the disc of the hind tibiae, they are sparse and simple (males)) (fig. 5.3). **2 (True bumblebees)**

- Hind tibiae convex and densely hairy (no corbiculum in females) (fig. 5.3).

  27 (Cuckoo bumblebees)

True bumblebees

2. Tip of abdomen pointed and enclosing sting (fig. 5.10). Abdomen with six segments visible from above. Antennae with twelve segments (fig. 5.6). **3 (females)**

- Tip of abdomen rounded and enclosing genital capsule (fig. 5.4). Abdomen with seven segments visible from above. Antennae with thirteen segments (fig. 5.6). **12 (males)**

Female (queen and worker) true bumblebees

Fig. 5.13
Mid-basitarsus
of
(a)
B.lapidarius
and
(b)
B.ruderarius

3. Black with red 'tail'. **4**

- Thorax with one or more yellow/pale bands. **5**

- Thorax orange-brown, without bands (may look banded if hairs worn off at centre of thorax, or have clusters of black hairs).**10**

4. Corbicular hairs black (but may be discoloured in old specimens, or by pollen). Mid basitarsus without spine (fig. 5.13a). Coat velvet-black, tail red. Sting sheath as fig. 5.31a (inner projections narrow). ***Bombus lapidarius***
   (Widespread and common in Essex)

- Corbicular hairs ginger (or black with ginger tips in workers). Coat sooty black, tail orange-red. Mid basitarsus with a spine (fig. 5.13b). Sting-sheath as in fig. 31b (inner projections wide). ***Bombus ruderarius***
  (Widespread but local in Essex. Declining)

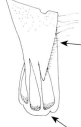

Fig. 5.14
Mandible of
B. terrestris

5. Thorax with one yellow band only (collar). Tail white, off-white or buff. **6**

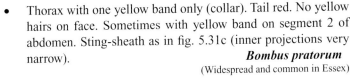

- Thorax with one yellow band only (collar). Tail red. No yellow hairs on face. Sometimes with yellow band on segment 2 of abdomen. Sting-sheath as in fig. 5.31c (inner projections very narrow).   ***Bombus pratorum***
(Widespread and common in Essex)

- Thorax with two yellow or pale bands (collar and scutellum). Tail white, off-white, or orange-red.   **7**

Fig. 5.15

Abdomen of worker
B. terrestris

6. Large. Yellow bands on collar and segment 2 of abdomen dull, golden yellow, often darkened and reduced. Tail buff. Notch and oblique groove on mandible (fig. 5.14). Sting sheath as in fig. 5.31d (similar to *B. lucorum*).   ***Bombus terrestris*** queen
(Widespread and common in Essex)

- As above, but smaller, and tail white or off-white. Narrow, brownish transitional zone between black hairs on the abdomen and white of the tail (fig. 5.15, use **x**10 lens). Notch and oblique groove on mandible (fig. 5.14).
Bombus terrestris worker
(Widespread and common in Essex)
[NB sometimes not distinguishable from *B. lucorum* worker]

- Yellow bands on collar and segment 2 of the abdomen pale lemon-yellow. Tail white, without brownish transitional zone (use **x**10 lens). Notch and oblique groove on mandible (fig. 5.14). Sting-sheath similar to *B. terrestris* (fig. 5.31e).
Bombus lucorum
(Widespread and common in Essex)
[NB workers not always distinguishable from *B. terrestris*]

Fig. 5.16

Mandible of
B. soroeensis

- Yellow bands on collar and segment 2 of the abdomen pale lemon yellow. Abdominal yellow band usually broken in mid-line. No notch or oblique groove on mandible (fig. 5.16 – use microscope). Inner projections of sting-sheath simple.
Bombus soroeensis
(Not so far recorded from Essex, probably declining nationally)

7. Bands on thorax lemon, golden, or brownish yellow. Tail white or off-white.   **8**

- Bands on thorax pale yellowish or greenish. Abdomen obscurely banded black and pale grey-green. Tail orange-red. Sting-sheath

Fig. 5.17a
Face of female
B. hortorum
(long)

Fig. 5.17b
Face of female
B. jonellus
(short)

Fig. 5.18a
Mandible of
B. hortorum
(oblique
groove, no
notch)

Fig. 5.18b
Mandible of
B. jonellus
(no oblique
groove, notch)

as in fig. 5.31f (inner projections wide).

Bombus sylvarum
(Rare. In Essex, confined to a few localities in the south)

8. Face long (fig. 5.17a). Mandibles with oblique groove but no notch (fig. 5.18a). Mid-basitarsus with spine (fig. 5.19a – difficult to see as surrounded by stiff hairs; use microscope).**9**

• Face short (fig. 5.17b). Mandibles without oblique groove, but with notch (fig. 5.18b). Mid-basitarsus without spine (fig. 5.19b). ***Bombus jonellus***
(Associated with heathland, moorland and coasts. One Essex record so far)

9. Yellow on scutellum narrower at middle than yellow on collar. Yellow hairs on segments one and two of abdomen. Sculpturing on tergite 6 of abdomen shallow (fig. 5.20a). Ventral plate 6 of abdomen without central keel. ***Bombus hortorum***
(Widespread and common in Essex)

• Yellow on scutellum as wide at middle as collar. Yellow on abdomen confined to segment 1. Yellow usually duller than in *B. hortorum*, and often reduced. Queens larger and more robust than queens of *B. hortorum*. Sculpturing on tergite 6 of abdomen deeper (fig. 5. 20b). Ventral plate 6 of abdomen without central keel. ***Bombus ruderatus***
(Extremely rare in Essex)
[NB distinction from *B. hortorum* and taxonomic status uncertain]

• Similar to dark forms of *B. ruderatus*, sometimes lacking yellow band on abdomen, but usually with pale fringes of hair on abdomen segments. Keel along mid line of ventral plate 6 of the abdomen (fig. 5.21 – use microscope).

Bombus subterraneus
(Probably extinct in Essex, and in Britain)

10. Hairs uneven in length. Variable admixture of black hairs on the abdomen (in pale specimens these may be inconspicuous - check sides of segments 2, 3 and 4, with lens). Sting sheath as fig. 5.31i (simple, relatively narrow inner projections).

Bombus pascuorum
(Widespread and common)

• Hairs more even in length, giving 'smart' appearance. No black hairs on the abdomen (use **x10** lens), but may be a brownish band on segment 2 of the abdomen. **11**

Fig. 5.19a
Mid-basitarsus
of *B. hortorum*
female

11. No black hairs on the thorax (check with **x**10 lens). Hairs at sides of segment 3 of abdomen rise from small 'bumps' (very difficult to see, even with microscope). Sting-sheath as in fig. 5.31j.   ***Bombus muscorum***
(In Essex very local on east coast and estuaries only)
[Small workers may not be distinguishable from *B. humilis*]

• Usually a few black hairs on the thorax, especially around the wing-bases and collar (use **x**10 lens – not, however, a reliable character). Hairs at sides of segment 3 of abdomen rise from tiny 'pits' (use microscope). Sting-sheath as in fig. 5.31k.
Bombus humilis
(In Essex, local, and confined to south, but may be common where it occurs)
[NB Small workers may be indistinguishable from *B. muscorum*]

Male true bumblebees

12. Thorax all black (may be a few pale hairs on collar and/or scutellum).   **13**

• Thorax with one or more yellow bands.   **15**

• Thorax mainly ginger-brown, sometimes with a few black hairs mixed in, but not forming a band.   **25**

Fig. 5.19b
Mid-basitarsus
of *B. jonellus*
female

13. Face short (as in fig. 5. 17b). Tail red. Genital capsule as in fig. 5.32a.   ***B. ruderarius*** (dark form)
(Widespread but local in Essex)

• Face long (as in fig. 5.17a). Tail white, grey, or blackish.   **14**

14. Black hairs on the mandibles. Hairs on rear edge of hind tibiae longer at the base, (fig. 5.23a). Genital capsule (fig. 5.32b) similar to *B. ruderatus*.   ***B. hortorum*** (dark forms)
(Widespread and common in Essex)
[NB May not be easily distinguished from dark forms of *B. ruderatus*]

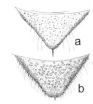

Fig. 5.20
Sculpturing of
dorsal surface
of final segment
of (a) *B. horto-*
rum and
(b) *B. ruderatus*

• Usually with ginger hairs on mandibles. Hairs on the rear edge of hind tibiae shorter at the base (fig. 5.23b). Genital capsule as in fig. 5.32c (similar to *B. hortorum*).
B. ruderatus (dark forms)
(Very rare in Essex)
[NB May not be easily distinguishable from dark forms of *B. hortorum]*

Fig. 5.21 Ventral surface of hind abdominal segment of *B. subterraneus* female

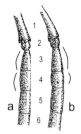

Fig. 5.22 Antennae of (a) *B. sylvarum* male and (b) *B. ruderarius* male

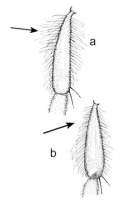

Fig. 5.23 Hind tibiae of (a) *B. hortorum* male and (b) *B. ruderatus* male

15. Thorax with one yellow band only (collar). Sometimes with yellow hairs on the scutellum, but not forming a band. Tail white, off-white, buff or red.   **16**

- Thorax with two yellow or pale yellow-green bands (collar and scutellum). Tail white, off-white or orange-red.   **19**

16. Tail red. Variable yellow band on collar (often yellow hairs on scutellum, but markedly less than on collar). Abdomen black, without yellow band. Yellow hairs on face. Genital capsule as in fig. 5.32d (sagittae barbed towards tip).
B. lapidarius
(Widespread and common in Essex)

- Tail red. Yellow band on collar wide and bright (often some yellow hairs on scutellum, but not forming distinct band). Usually wide yellow band on segment 2 of abdomen. Yellow hairs on the face. Genital capsule as in fig. 5.32e (sagittae tapering to incurved hooks). *B. pratorum*
(Widespread and common in Essex)

- Tail white, off-white or buff. (If tail red, then hind basitarsi as in fig. 5.24b, and face black)   **17**

17. Hind basitarsi slender at the base, and with long hairs on the rear edge (fig. 5.24b). Third segment of antennae shorter than the fifth (fig. 5.25a). Genital capsule as in fig. 5.32f (tips of sagittae tapered to outward-directed hooks).
B. soroeensis
(Not recorded in Essex)

- Hind basitarsi wide at the base and with short hairs on the rear edge (5.24a). Third and fifth segments of antennae roughly the same length (fig. 5.25b). Genital capsule as fig. 5.32g or h; (sagittae not as above).   **18**

18. Collar and band on segment two of the abdomen pale lemon-yellow (in pale specimens yellow hairs on scutellum, wider band on abdomen). Usually with yellow hairs on the face. Tail white. Genital capsule as in fig. 5.32g (similar to *B. terrestris).*
B. lucorum
(Widespread and common in Essex)

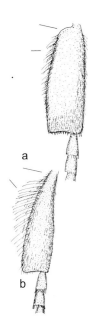

a

b

Fig. 5.24 Hind
basitarsi of
(a) *B. lucorum*
male and (b)
B. soroeensis
male

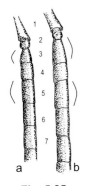

a   b

Fig. 5.25
Antennae of (a)
B. soroeensis,
male and
(b) *B. lucorum*
male

- Collar and band on segment two of the abdomen dull golden-yellow. No yellow hairs on the face. Tail off-white to buff. Genital capsule as in fig. 5.32h (similar to *B. lucorum*).
  B. terrestris
  (Widespread and common in Essex)

19. Face short (as fig. 5.17b). **20**

- Face long (as fig. 5.17a). **24**

20. Tail white (sometimes with yellow or reddish hairs). **21**

- Tail pale yellow, or red. **22**

21. Tail white. Yellow hairs on face. Genital capsule as in fig. 5.32g (sagittae swollen towards tip, and curved slightly outwards).
  B. lucorum (pale forms)

- Tail usually white (sometimes with yellow or reddish hairs). Yellow hairs on face. Genital capsule as in fig. 5.32i (sagittae taper to inwardly pointing hooks). **B. jonellus**
  (One record only from Essex)

22. Abdomen mainly pale yellow. Genital capsule as fig. 5.32j, volsellae small and inconspicuous. **B. subterraneus**
  (Probably extinct in Britain)

- Tail red or orange-red. Genital capsule: volsellae large, tapering to pointed apex. **23**

23. Third antennal segment much longer than the fourth (fig. 5.22(b)). Genital capsule (fig. 5.32a) similar to *B. sylvarum* but with pointed inner projections of volsellae. **B. ruderarius**
  (Widespread but local in Essex)

- Third antennal segment roughly equal to or only slightly longer than the fourth (fig. 5. 22(a)). Genital capsule as in fig. 5.32k (similar to *B. ruderarius* but with blunt inner projection of volsellae). **B. sylvarum**
  (Rare. In Essex, confined to a few localities in the south)

24. Yellow band on the scutellum narrower in the middle than the collar. Hairs on the the mandibles black. Hairs on the rear edge

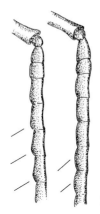

a   b

Fig. 5.26
Antennae of
(a)
B. pascuorum,
male and
(b)
B. muscorum
male

of the hind tibiae longer at the base (fig. 5.23(a)). Genital capsule as in fig. 5.32b (similar to *B.ruderatus*).

B. hortorum
(Widespread and common in Essex)

- Yellow band on the scutellum as wide at the middle as the collar. Hairs on the mandibles ginger. Hairs on the rear edge of the hind tibiae shorter at the base (fig. 5.23b). Genital capsule as in fig. 5.32c (similar to *B. hortorum*).

B. ruderatus
(Very rare in Essex)
Not always easily separated from *B.hortorum*

25. Abdomen with a mixture of ginger-brown and black hairs. In some examples the black hairs are inconspicuous - check sides of middle segments of the abdomen with a x10 lens. Middle segments of the antennae asymmetrically swollen below (fig. 5.26a). Genital capsule as in fig. 5.32l (volsellae small, sagittae taper to tip).

B. pascuorum
(Widespread and common in Essex)

- Abdomen without black hairs on dorsal surface. Swellings on underside of the middle and outer segments of the antennae less marked, and symmetrical (fig 5.26b).   **26**

26. Thorax often (but not always) with a few black hairs (check collar and near the wing-bases, using x10 lens). Genital capsule as in fig. 5.32m (volsellae projecting to point at apex).

B. humilis
(Confined to the south in Essex, but may be locally common)

- Thorax without black hairs (check with x10 lens). Genital capsule as in fig. 5.32n (volsellae with blunt, rounded apex).

B. muscorum
(Very local in Essex - east coast estuarine marshes only)

Cuckoo bumblebees

27. Large. Tip of the abdomen pointed and enclosing sting. Variously shaped 'callosities' on ventral surface of final abdominal segment (see fig. 5.33). Antennae with 12 segments (fig. 5.6).

28 (females)

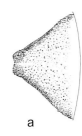

a

b

Fig. 5.27
Dorsal surface
of final abdomi-
nal segment of
(a)
B.(P.) vestalis,
female and
(b)
*B.(P.) bohemi-
cus* female

- Smaller. Tip of abdomen rounded, and enclosing genital capsule (fig. 5.34). No callosities on ventral surface of final abdominal segment. Antennae with thirteen segments (fig. 5.6).
  32 (males)

A: Female cuckoo bumblebees

Note: Colour patterns are included for provisional guidance, but are variable and not reliable for definitive identification. Callosities on the ventral surface of the final abdominal segment are good diagnostic features.

28. Black with red tail, and darkened wings. Very large callosities on underside of final abdominal segment (see fig. 5.33a).
    B. (P.) rupestris
    (Currently rare in Essex, but increasing in some parts of range.
    Nest parasite of *B.lapidarius*)

- One or more yellow bands on the thorax (occasionally none). Tail mainly white or yellowish.   **29**

29. Tail yellow. Callosities form conspicuous shallow 'V' shape (fig. 5.33b).
    B. (P.) campestris
    (Widespread but local in Essex. Nest parasite of *B. pascuorum*)

- Tail white with yellow 'flashes' at the sides.   **30**

- Tail white without yellow flashes.   **31**

30. Coat relatively short and even. Dorsal surface of final segment of the abdomen pitted and dull (fig. 5.27a). Callosities on ventral surface of final abdominal segment as in fig. 5.33c (less strongly curved in lateral view (ii), and set further apart at the apex (i)).   ***B. (P.) vestalis***
    (Widespread and common in Essex. Nest parasite of *B. terrestris*)

- Coat relatively long and uneven. Dorsal surface of final segment of the abdomen shiny (fig. 5.27b). Callosities on ventral surface of final abdominal segment as in fig. 5.33d, (more strongly curved in lateral view (ii) and set closer together at the apex (i)).
  B. (P.) bohemicus
  (Not recorded from Essex)

31. Thorax usually with one yellow band (collar) only. Tip of the abdomen tightly curved under the body. Dorsal surface of

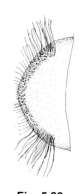

Fig. 5.28
Ventral surface of final abdominal segment of male *B.(P.) campestris*, male

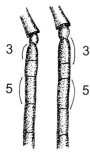

a   b

Fig. 5.29
Antennae of (a) *B.(P.) campestris* and (b) *B.(P.) sylvestris*, males

final abdominal segment shiny and without keel. Callosities on ventral surface of final abdominal segment very small and inconspicuous (fig. 5.33e).   ***B. (P.) sylvestris***
(Widespread in Essex. Nest parasite of *B. pratorum*)

• Thorax with one or two yellow bands (collar and scutellum). Dorsal surface of final abdominal segment dull and with keel along the middle. Callosities on ventral surface of final abdominal segment form a shallow 'u' shape (fig. 5.33f).
B. (P.) barbutellus
(Widespread in Essex. Nest parasite of *B. hortorum*)

• Thorax with one yellow band (collar) only. Dorsal surface of final segment of abdomen dull and pitted, without keel along the middle (fig. 5.27a). Callosities on ventral surface of final abdominal segment as in fig. 5.33c.   ***B. (P.) vestalis***
(faded specimen, lacking yellow 'flashes')

B: Male cuckoo bumblebees

32. All, or almost all, hairs on thorax and abdomen black.   **33**

• Thorax and abdomen black with or without yellow bands. Tail red. Genital capsule: squamae with pointed inner projecton bearing long, curved hairs, and sagittae with tooth-like projection below (fig. 5.34a).   ***B. (P.) rupestris***

• Thorax and abdomen black with or without yellow bands. Tail white, yellow, or white with yellow 'flashes'.   **34**

33. Ventral surface of the final abdominal segment with tufts of long, black hair on each side (fig. 5.28). Third segment of antennae shorter than the fifth (fig. 5.29a). Genital capsule: volsellae wide and triangular (fig. 5.34b) . ***B. (P.) campestris***
(melanic form)

• Ventral surface of final abdominal segment without long hair-tufts. Third antennal segment about equal in length to the fifth (fig. 5.29b). Genital capsule: volsellae small and narrowly elongate (fig. 5.34c).   ***B. (P.) sylvestris***
(melanic form)

a

b

Fig 5.30

Ventral surface
of the final
abdominal
segment of
(a)
B.(P.) vestalis
male and
(b)
B.(P.)
barbutellus
male

34. Tail mainly yellow. Tufts of long black hair on each side of
the ventral surface of the final abdominal segment (fig. 5.28).
Genital capsule: volsellae wide and triangular (fig. 5.34b)

B.(P.) campestris
(pale forms)

• Tail white, or white with yellow 'flashes'. Without tufts of
long black hair at sides of ventral surface of final abdominal
segment.   **35**

35. Third and fifth segments of antennae about equal in length (fig.
5.29b).   **36**

• Third antennal segment shorter than the fifth (fig. 5.29a). **37**

36. Tail yellowish or whitish, but with black hairs on the final (7th)
segment. Genital capsule: volsellae large and triangular, inner
projection of squamae pointed (fig. 5.34d).

B. (P.) bohemicus
(Not recorded in Essex)

• Tail white or off-white, but (usually) with ginger hairs on final
(7th) segment. Genital capsule: volsellae small and narrowly
elongate, squamae without pointed inner projection (fig. 5.34c).

B. (P.) sylvestris
(usual colour form)

37. Tail usually white with yellow 'flashes' at the sides, but these
fade to white in older specimens. Tip of ventral surface of final
abdominal segment without small mounds (fig. 5.30a). Genital
capsule: volsellae pointed at apex (fig. 5.34e).

B. (P.) vestalis

• Tail white or off-white. Tip of ventral surface of final segment
of the abdomen with small mounds on either side of the mid-
line (fig. 5.30b). Genital capsule: volsellae rounded at the apex
(fig. 5.34f).   *B. (P.) barbutellus*

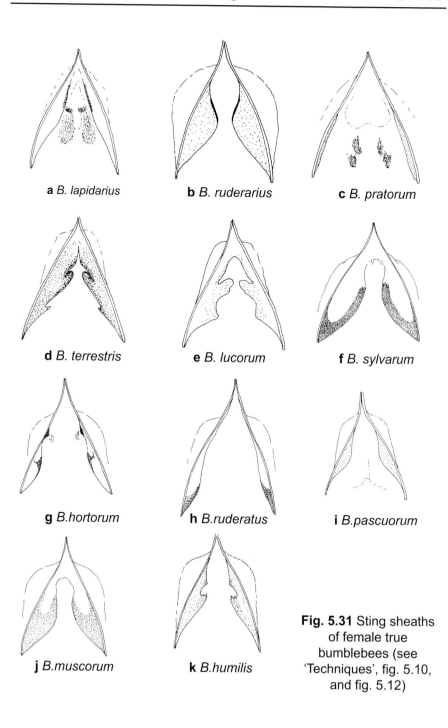

a *B. lapidarius*

b *B. ruderarius*

c *B. pratorum*

d *B. terrestris*

e *B. lucorum*

f *B. sylvarum*

g *B.hortorum*

h *B.ruderatus*

i *B.pascuorum*

j *B.muscorum*

k *B.humilis*

Fig. 5.31 Sting sheaths of female true bumblebees (see 'Techniques', fig. 5.10, and fig. 5.12)

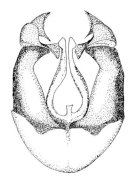

a *B. ruderarius*

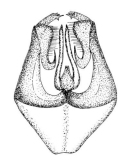

b *B. hortorum*

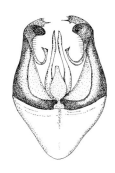

c *B. ruderatus*

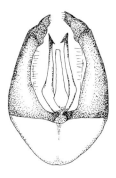

d *B. lapidarius*

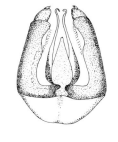

e *B. pratorum*

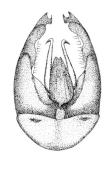

f *B. soroeensis*

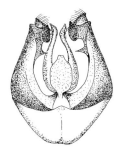

g *B. lucorum*

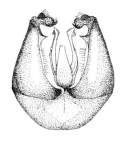

h *B. terrestris*

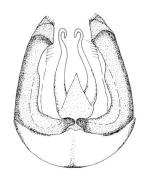

i *B. jonellus*

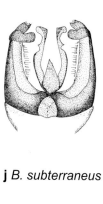

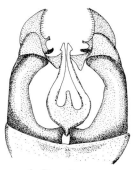

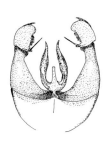

j *B. subterraneus*   **k** *B. sylvarum*   **l** *B. pascuorum*

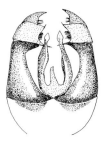

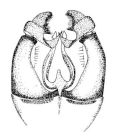

Fig 5.32 Genital capsules of male true bumblebees (see 'Techniques' and figs 5.4 and 5.11)

m *B. humilis*   **n** *B. muscorum*

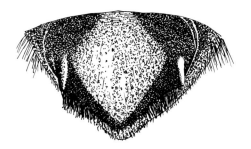

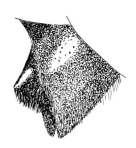

a(i) *B.(P.) rupestris* ventral view   **a(ii)** lateral view

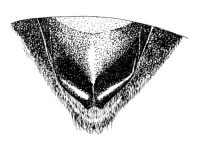

b(i) *B.(P.) campestris* ventral view   **b(ii)** lateral view

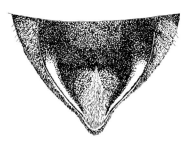

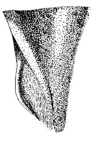

c(i) *B.(P.) vestalis* ventral view   **c(ii)** lateral view

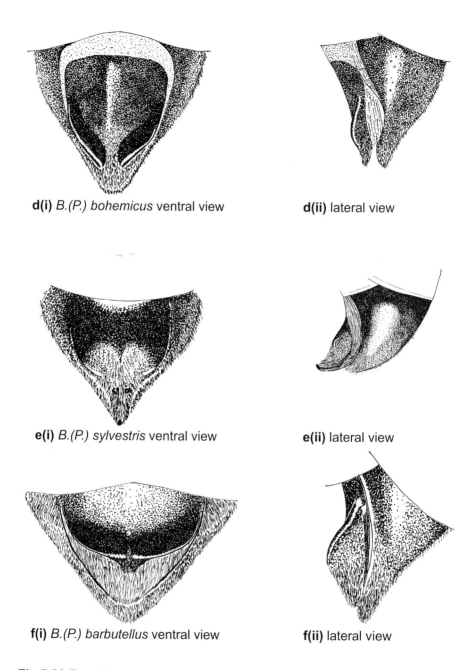

d(i) *B.(P.) bohemicus* ventral view   **d(ii)** lateral view

e(i) *B.(P.) sylvestris* ventral view   **e(ii)** lateral view

f(i) *B.(P.) barbutellus* ventral view   **f(ii)** lateral view

Fig 5.33 Female cuckoo bumblebees: callosities on final abdominal sternites

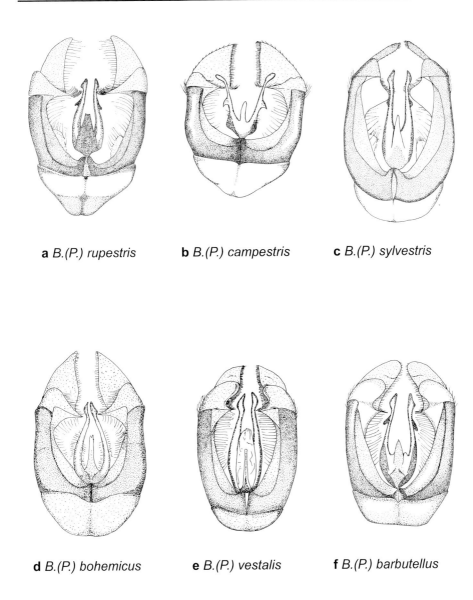

a *B.(P.) rupestris*   **b** *B.(P.) campestris*   **c** *B.(P.) sylvestris*

d *B.(P.) bohemicus*   **e** *B.(P.) vestalis*   **f** *B.(P.) barbutellus*

Fig. 5.34 Genital capsules of male cuckoo bumblebees (subgenus *Psithyrus*)

Introduction

Prior to the present survey, there were reliable records of 17 species of bumblebees from Essex: 12 'true' bumblebees and five 'cuckoos' (subgenus *Psithyrus*). Of these, 16 have been re-found during the survey and a further species added to the list. These 17, together with the one species now believed extinct in the county (*Bombus subterraneus*), are the subjects of the following species-accounts. A further two species (*B. soroeensis*, and *B.(P.) bohemicus*) do occur in other parts of south and south-east England, and could well be present, undiscovered, in Essex. For this reason, and to make this work more useful outside the boundaries of Essex, these species have been included in the Key (chapter 5), and distinctive features have been given in the 'Identification' sections of the species-accounts of similar species (*B. hortorum, B. lucorum* and *B.(P.) vestalis*, respectively). They are not, however, given separate species-accounts in this chapter.

As mentioned elsewhere, recent research, especially the work of Paul Williams, has called into question previous understanding of the evolutionary affinities among bumblebees. However, as Williams (1998) notes more work is needed for a precise understanding of the relationships among them to be established. The order followed in the species-accounts in this chapter represents a compromise between current scientific thinking and ease of use for the field naturalist. First are five of the widespread and common species which beginners will need to familiarise themselves with. The sequence is then interrupted by accounts of two rare, possibly extinct, species (*B. ruderatus* and *B. subterraneus*) which resemble one of the more common species (*B. hortorum*). These are followed by another similar-looking species, *B. jonellus*. Next comes the sixth and last of the common species of 'true' bumblebees (*B. pascuorum*). This is placed next to two close relatives ('carder' bumblebees, subgenus *Thoracobombus*) which are very similar in appearance, but much more scarce (*B. humilis* and *B. muscorum*). Then come two more 'carder' bees, *B. ruderarius* and *B. sylvarum* (the shrill carder bee). Finally, the five Essex species of 'cuckoo' bumblebees of the subgenus *Psithyrus* are described.

The most recent and authoritative systematic classification of the known world bumblebee fauna is Williams (1998). His provisional ordering is based on a cladistic classification which places *Psithyrus* within the genus *Bombus*. Table 6.1 is a systematic ordering of the species dealt with in this work, derived from Williams's checklist.

The British distribution maps

These are derived from the IBRA/ITE *Atlas* maps, the areas of dark shading being vice-counties with a record from 1960 onwards. Light shading represents vice-counties with only pre-1960 records. It must be emphasised that care is needed in

Table 6.1 List of species dealt with in this work

Genus *Bombus* Latreille (broad sense)	
Subgenus *Psithyrus* Lepeletier *Bombus (Ps.) vestalis* (Geoffroy) *Bombus (Ps.) bohemicus* Seidl *Bombus (Ps.) barbutellus* (Kirby) *Bombus (Ps.) rupestris* (Fabricius) *Bombus (Ps.) campestris* (Panzer) *Bombus (Ps.) sylvestris* (Lepeletier) **Subgenus *Thoracobombus* Dalla Torre** *Bombus (Th.) muscorum* (Linnaeus) *Bombus (Th.) humilis* Illiger *Bombus (Th.) ruderarius* (Müller) *Bombus (Th.) sylvarum* (Linnaeus) *Bombus (Th.) pascuorum* (Scopoli) **Subgenus *Megabombus* Dalla Torre** *Bombus (Mg.) hortorum* (Linnaeus) *Bombus (Mq.) ruderatus* (Fabricius)*	**Subgenus *Kallobombus* Dalla Torre** *Bombus (Kl.) soroeensis* (Fabricius) **Subgenus *Subterraneobombus* Vogt** *Bombus (St.) subterraneus* (Linnaeus) **Subgenus *Pyrobombus* Dalla Torre** *Bombus (Pr.) pratorum* (Linnaeus) *Bombus (Pr.) jonellus* (Kirby) **Subgenus *Bombus* (strict sense)** *Bombus (Bo.) terrestris* (Linnaeus) *Bombus (Bo.) lucorum* (Linnaeus) **Subgenus *Melanobombus* Dalla Torre** *Bombus (M.) lapidarius* (Linnaeus)*

the interpretation of these maps. The *Atlas* was published in 1980, but almost all the data were collected prior to the mid-1970s. Major contractions of range for many of the rarer and more localised species have occurred since that time. For most of these species, the maps gave an over-optimistic picture of distribution even at the time of their publication and the situation is now considerably worse. It should also be noted that using areas as large as vice-counties as the recording unit also tends to give a more optimistic picture, as a species may be very localised within such a unit.

5 km square Essex maps

These are based on exactly the same data set as the tetrad maps and include only post-1980 records. For the more widespread species, these maps give a better indication of range in Essex than the tetrad maps since they are less affected by unevenness of coverage in the survey. The number of species per 5 km square recorded for 1980 onwards is shown here. Seven species is the minimum expected from a well-surveyed square.

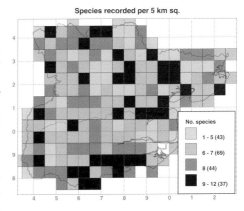

Species recorded per 5 km sq.

No. species

- 1 - 5 (43)
- 6 - 7 (69)
- 8 (44)
- 9 - 12 (37)

Essex Tetrad maps indicate with reasonable precision the position of each observation. For the common and widespread species, blank tetrads indicate lack of recording, rather than absence of bees.

Species recorded per tetrad (2 km sq.)

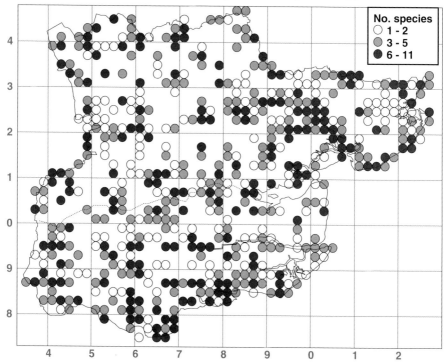

Forage source charts

The tables list all observations of flower-visits by the relevant caste and species that were noted during the survey. They include Essex data only, and generally do not discriminate between 'rob' vists, visits for nectar, pollen or both (V). Where pollen collection could be confirmed, this is indicated (P). In the case of cultivated flowers, either the scientific or vernacular names have been listed, depending on which seemed likely to be the more familiar to the reader. In some cases, bees were observed visiting a wide variety of garden flowers and shrubs, many of which could not be readily identified (Misc. (g)). Some visits to agricultural crops were observed (a). In some cases foraging bees could be identified without capture down to species but not caste. Finally, the tables give no indication of which plant species are most frequently visited by the bees. The shorter lists given in the text are more selective, and are generally based on (subjective) estimates of the 'preferred' forage plants for each caste and species through the flight-period. In some cases a small number of exceptionally early or late observations have been excluded.

Bombus lucorum (Linnaeus)

White-tailed bumblebee

This is a common species, found throughout the county in a wide variety of habitats.

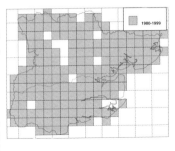

Description

Queens are predominantly black, with a single yellow band (collar) at the front of the thorax, and another at the front end (tergite 2) of the abdomen. The rear segments of the abdomen (tail) are white. The face is approximately as wide as it is long. The yellow bands are generally of a pale, lemon shade. The sting sheath is as shown in fig. 5.31e.

Workers are similar to the queens, but generally considerably smaller in size. They can be difficult to distinguish from the workers of *B. terrestris*, which also generally have white, or whitish tails (see comments under that species).

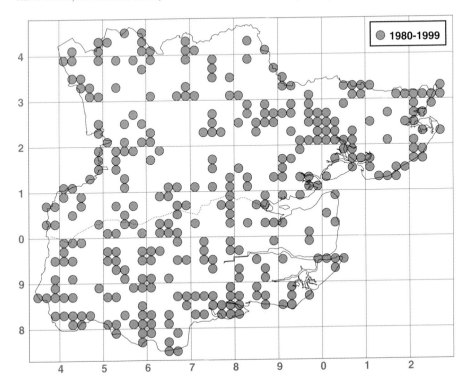

Males are rather variable. Darker forms resemble the females, with the addition of a tuft of yellow hairs on the face. Paler forms are more extensively yellow, with wider pale yellow bands on the collar and abdomen, some yellow hairs on the hind margin of the thorax (scutellum), and yellow hair on the head and face.

Identification

The pattern of two yellow stripes and a white tail is distinctive for the queens. The same pattern plus the yellow face serves to identify the males. In the case of the pale forms of the male, confusion with *B. hortorum* is possible, but the long face and lack of yellow on the face of the latter are reliable characters. Workers of this species and *B. terrestris* are often difficult to distinguish.

B. soroeensis, not so far recorded from Essex, is similar in colour pattern. However, queens and workers usually have the abdominal yellow band broken in the middle and lack the oblique groove and notch on the mandibles, which are characteristic of *B. lucorum* (and *B. terrestris*). In males, the third antennal segment is shorter than the fifth in *B. soroeensis* but approximately equal in length in *B lucorum*. There are also differences in the hind basitarsi (see the main key in chapter 5), and the male genital capsules are markedly different (see fig. 5.32 f & g).

Life-history

Queens of this species are among the earliest to emerge from hibernation in the spring, and there is some evidence of continued activity throughout the year in south Essex. In north Essex, queens are usually first observed during March (25/3/97, 7/3/98, 27/3/99). Initially they forage to meet their own nutritional needs on a range of spring-flowering plants, notably sallows, *Prunus* spp., white deadnettle and various garden herbs and shrubs. From late March, or the beginning of April, they may be observed prospecting for nest sites. When engaged in this, they fly close to the ground, systematically investigating the contours of areas of rough, tussocky grass or other rank vegetation, often in the vicinity of scrub. One was observed exploring crevices in a garden rockery in Colchester on 24/4/1987. Nest-site prospecting is not commonly observed after mid April, but may continue into May (latest date observed 7/5/90).

During this period the queens may also be observed with full pollen loads on the hind legs (*e.g.* 29/03/00, Colchester), signifying that a nest has already been established. The nests are usually below ground, in holes, and often in disused nests of small mammals. The first workers appear during April (11/4/99) and may be observed foraging from a wide variety of both wild and cultivated flowering plants throughout the spring and summer months into September. A nest was observed on 31/5/97 in a hole in the south-facing slope of the old railway cutting at Dunmow. Workers were noted leaving and then re-entering the nest with pollen loads from nearby stands of hoary plantain.

The first males and young queens emerge from late May onwards (first males 25/5/97, 3/6/98). Males may be observed until mid-August, with sporadic sightings of females into October or November (7/10/99, 6/11/99 (Suffolk)). Males engaged in 'patrolling' behaviour fly close to the ground and circle round tree-trunks or fence posts (Fussell & Corbet, 1992c). Mating is not commonly observed, but the extraordinary event of a male *B. lapidarius* mating with a female *B. lucorum* was noted at Maldon on 17/7/94!

The above timings apply to the north of Essex (and probably to most of the rest of the county) but a remarkable series of observations in the Southend area indicate year-round activity in queens of this species in some years, and even suggests the possibility that some colonies may survive the winter. Queens of *B. lucorum* were observed feeding in a garden in Thundersley on 1/12/98 (on *Fuchsia*), 5/12/98 (on *Hebe*), 15/2/99, 9/11/99 (on *Hebe*). Also what were probably workers of this species were observed in the same garden from 11/2/98 onwards, in increasing numbers (correspondence, D.G. Down and R.G. Payne). I observed a queen of this species collecting pollen from *Chaenomeles* (Japonica) flowers in public gardens at Westcliff-on-Sea on 8/2/98.

Discussion

This species is referred to in Prŷs-Jones & Corbet (1991) as having a long life-cycle, with no evidence for a second cycle of colony activity in each season. Essex observations cast some doubt on this. Whereas Prŷs-Jones & Corbet give May as the date for first appearance of workers, they are regularly observed in April in north Essex, and as early as February in the extreme south of the county. It seems likely that annual variations in spring weather, as well as quite localised differences in aspect and climate determine the date at which the queens first become active and begin nesting activity.

This table excludes unusually early and late observations - see text							
Queen	F	M	A	M	J	J	A
Japonica (g)	P						
Rosemary (g)	V						
Sallow (in)		P	V				
Sallow (f)		V					
Cherry plum		V					
White deadnettle		P	V	V			
Heathers (g)		V					
Flowering currant (g)		V					
Blackthorn			V				
Bluebell			V	V			
Oil-seed rape (a)			V				
Rhododendron				V	V		
Common vetch				V			
Gorse				V			
Comfrey				V	V		
Green alkanet				V			
Rose (g)				V			
Field bean (a)				V			
Bramble					V	V	V
Creeping cinquefoil					V		
Marsh thistle					V		
Creeping thistle					V		V
Hebe(g)					V		V
Honeysuckle (g)					V		
Lavender (g)					P		
Purple toadflax (g)					V		
Meadow vetchling						V	
Rosebay willow-herb						V	
Spear thistle						V	V
Knapweed						V	V
Wild angelica							V
Devil's-bit scabious							V
Hoary ragwort							V
Buddleia (g)							V
Busy Lizzy (g)							V
Dahlia (g)							V
Lavatera (g)							V

Worker	A	M	J	J	A	S
Miscel. (g)	V		V	V		V
Creeping buttercup		P'				
Wild rose		V				
Midland hawthorn		V				
Common vetch		P'				
Broom		V	P			
Comfrey		V	V			
White deadnettle		V				
Hoary plantain		P'				
Slender thistle		V				
Broom (g)		V				
Bramble			P	V		
Creeping cinquefoil			V			
Bird's-foot trefoil			V			
Bush vetch			V			
White clover			V	V		
Red clover			V			
Tree lupin			P'			
Hogweed			V			
Hedge woundwort			V			
Wood sage			V			
Aster (g)			V			
Bellflower (g)			V			
Hebe (g)		'	V	V		
Lavender (g)			V			
Red-hot poker (g)			V			
St John's wort (9)			V			
Snowberry (g)			V			
Mallow				V		
Melilot				V		
Rosebay willowherb				V		
Black horehound				V		
Teasel				V		
Spear thistle				V		
Marsh thistle				V		
Creeping thistle				V		
Privet (g)				V		
Red bartsia					V	
Buddleia (g)					V	
Busy Lizzy (g)					V	
Ivy (p)						V

Even in the north of the county, observations are at least consistent with double cycles in some years. Workers collecting pollen from ivy on 19/9/97 at Petches Bridge, near Braintree, and also collecting pollen from ornamental flower-baskets at Halstead on 6/9/98 indicate active colonies well into September. It seems possible that queens noted in October and November could be progeny from such late colonies. Further evidence consistent with multiple cycles is the observation of a young queen of this species with full pollen loads, foraging from lavender in a garden at Alresford on 30/6/99. Interestingly, however, there appear to be no records of males of this species later than the end of August. If there are second-generation colonies, then it may be that they do not survive long enough to produce sexual forms, or produce only females. Another possibility is that there are wide differences in the timing of initial establishment of nests by over-wintered queens, since prospecting for nest-sites is observed from the end of March through to early May. This would lead to a staggering of the emergence of males and females through the summer. Clearly, more systematic research on this topic is needed.

Habitat and forage-sources

A survey of nesting sites conducted by Fussell & Corbet (1992a) using amateur observers did not discriminate between this species and *B. terrestris*. However, their results suggest that these species generally nest underground, often close to trees or shrubs, and quite commonly on or under the floors of buildings such as garden sheds and outhouses. In common with other species, sites sheltered from the wind are chosen. A study by the same authors (Fussell & Corbet, 1991) on a Cambridgeshire farm (which also did not discriminate between this species and *B. terrestris*) gave black horehound, bramble, spear thistle and hogweed as the most commonly visited forage plants. Although short-tongued bees such as *B. lucorum* did visit flowers of field bean, they

Male	A	M	J	J	A
Ground ivy		V			
Red campion		V			
Bramble			V	V	
Creeping cinquefoil			V		
White clover			V		
Hogweed			V		
Slender thistle			V		
Creeping thistle			V	V	
Hawkweed			V		
Bellflower (g)			V		
Hebe (g)			V	V	V
Purple toadflax (g)			V		
Thyme (g)			V		
Misc. shrubs & herbs (g)			V		
Rosebay willowherb				V	
Teasel				V	
Lesser burdock				V	
Spear thistle				V	
Knapweed				V	V
Rose (g)				V	
Wild angelica					V
Lavatera (g)					V
Passion flower (g)					V

Caste unspecified	A	M	J	J	A
Comfrey		V		V	
Bugle		V			
Mallow			V		
Birds-foot trefoil			V		
Fodder vetch			V		
Common vetch			V		
Thistles			V		
Sea lavender				V	
Rosebay willowherb				V	
Wood sage				V	
Honeysuckle				V	
Greater knapweed				V	
Lavatera (g)				V	
Lavender (g)				V	
Spiny restharrow					V
Knapweed					V
Ragwort					V
Hoary ragwort					V

tended to rob the flowers by nectaring through holes bitten through the base of the corolla, or visited extra-floral nectaries on stipules of the plant. They therefore probably played little role in pollination.

Fussell & Corbet (1991) argued that bumblebees on farmland require areas of ungrazed permanent grassland with a range of perennial flowers providing a supply of nectar and pollen throughout the flight-period. Uncultivated field-corners, hedgerows with ditches, grassy banks, cart-tracks, motorway and roadside verges are likely to provide both forage sources and nesting sites. They also note that sightings of short-tongued species were sporadic, indicating use of off-site forage sources.

Observations in Essex are broadly consistent with these findings. *B. lucorum* is found in a wide variety of habitats, including roadside and motorway verges, remaining hedgerows, woodland rides, and river-banks as well as marginal habitat on farmland. Rough grassland surrounding mineral extraction sites, and ruderal habitats provided by neglected former industrial sites, sustain an abundance of suitable forage plants. Along with several other species that remain common and widespread, *B. lucorum* is a familiar sight in suburban gardens, urban parks and public open spaces. It is unclear how important such habitats are as nesting sites, but they are clearly vital in meeting nutritional needs of colonies. Queens observed during the winter months were feeding exclusively on garden flowers such as *Fuchsia*, *Hebe* and *Erica*. In early spring queens of this species take both pollen and nectar from sallows, and also forage from *Prunus* spp., white deadnettle and bluebell in semi-natural habitats. However, they also frequent parks and gardens, where they use a wide variety of herbaceous and shrubby garden plants (*Japonica*, *Rosmarinus*, *Ribes*, *Rhododendron*, *Rosa*, *Erica*, *Calluna* and many others) as forage sources. Queens also visit agricultural crops such as field bean and oil-seed rape. Young queens, emerging from early June onwards, visit a wide range of wild flowers, most especially bramble and comfrey, as well as various Asteraceae, such as thistles and knapweeds and Dipsacaeae (scabious). Cultivated plants also visited during the summer months include *Lonicera*, *Hebe*, *Lavandula*, *Lavatera*, *Linaria purpurea* and *Buddleia*.

Workers of this species are also partial to a wide range of garden shrubs and flowers such as *Genista*, *Aster*, *Campanula*, *Hebe*, *Lavandula*, *Symphoricarpos*, *Ligustrum*, *Buddleia* and many more. Bramble is an important forage source, notably for pollen in June and July. In addition workers visit a wide variety of wild flowers including several Fabaceae (bird's-foot trefoil, vetches, clovers and broom), Asteraceae (various thistles), and Lamiaceae (hedge woundwort, black horehound and wood sage). In August and September red bartsia and then ivy are important, in addition to cultivated species. Males are similarly catholic in their foraging habits, visiting both cultivated and wild flowers. *Hebe*, *Lavatera*, *Rosa*, *Thymus* and *Campanula* spp. are among the former, whilst the Asteraceae, particularly thistles and knapweed, are especially favoured among the wild species.

Distribution and status in Essex

This species is widely distributed and common throughout the British Isles. Morley (1899) regarded *B. lucorum* as a subspecies of *B. terrestris*, referring to it as 'apparently common'. Harwood (1884) listed it among the species to be found in the neighbourhood of Colchester. Chapman (1962-66) regarded it as 'one of our commonest bumblebees': this remains true today. During the current survey it was recorded from 332 tetrads spread across all 57 ten-kilometre squares in the county.

Bombus terrestris (Linnaeus)

Buff-tailed bumblebee

This is a common and widespread species in a wide variety of habitats throughout the county.

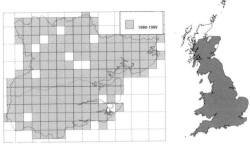

Description

Queens are usually very large. As with *B. lucorum*, the coat is mainly black, with two yellow bands, one on the collar, the other on segment two of the abdomen. These are usually of a duller hue than in *B. lucorum*, tending to a golden or even brownish yellow. The abdominal yellow band is narrowed in some specimens, and the yellow band on the collar is often very narrow and dark. The tail is typically buff, but is sometimes only slightly off-white, or may be pale brown.

Workers are much smaller than the queens, but are similarly coloured except for the

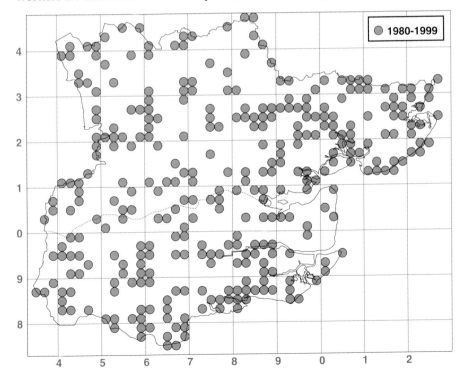

tail. This is usually white, leading to easy confusion with workers of *B. lucorum*. In general, workers of *B. terrestris* resemble the queens in having duller, golden yellow bands, compared with the paler, lemon yellow of the bands in typical *B. lucorum* workers. Darker specimens of *B. terrestris*, with reduced yellow bands, are distinctive. Another useful character is best observed by tubing a specimen, suppressing its movements as indicated in chapter 1 and examining the tail with a hand lens. In *B. lucorum* there is usually a sharp boundary between the black hairs on the abdomen and the white tail, whereas in *B. terrestris* workers, there is a transitional brownish zone (fig. 5.15). There are slight differences in the structure of the sting sheaths but these are less clear in the workers. In any case these differences are of no use for identification in the field.

Males are very similar in appearance to the females, though usually somewhat smaller. In specimens observed in Essex the tail varies from slightly off-white to pale buff. The male genitalia are as shown in fig. 5.32h.

Identification

Large size, two dull yellow bands, and buff tail serve to distinguish the queens quite readily. Workers are often difficult, and sometimes impossible to distinguish from those of *B. lucorum* in the field. However, when large numbers are foraging together it is usually possible to assign at least some individuals to one species or the other. More often than not the two species share forage-sites. The males are readily distinguished from those of *B. lucorum*, having much reduced and duller yellow bands. They also lack the yellow hairs on the face. They are, however, less easy to distinguish from young queens during the summer months when both may be seen foraging prior to the latter entering their hibernation sites. Males can often be picked out by their generally more lethargic approach to foraging. Closer examination is then needed to confirm the extra antennal segment, and the more rounded tip to the abdomen.

Life-history

As with *B. lucorum*, there are significant differences in flight periods, and possibly in reproductive cycles as between the extreme south of the county and elsewhere. *B. terrestris* queens are usually among the first to emerge from hibernation, though the dates vary from year to year (13/2/98, 12/3/99 at Colchester). They seem particularly attracted to sallow catkins, as well as to various early-flowering cultivated shrubs. They are by far the most frequently observed species in early spring as they alternate between foraging, sunning themselves on warm days, and prospecting for nest sites. They engage in this activity soon after emerging from hibernation (as early as late February), and their behaviour resembles that of *B. lucorum*. One was observed for ten minutes systematically 'contouring' an area of tufted long grass, leaf litter and stinging nettles adjacent to hawthorn scrub at University of Essex campus on 25/3/99. Similar

Queen	F	M	A	M	J	J	A	S	O
Sallow (m)	V	P	V						
Flowering currant (g)	V		V						
Heather(g)	V	V							
Honeysuckle (g)	V								
Viburnum (g)	V								
Sallow (mf)		V	V						
Cherry plum		V							
Blackthorn		V	V						
Dandelion		V							
Crab apple			V						
Gorse			P						
White deadnettle			V	V					
Bluebell			V						
Dogwood				V					
Lilac				V					V
Oil-seed rape (a)				V					
Red campion					V				
Mallow					V				
Bramble					P	V			
Creeping thistle					V				
Aster (g)					V				
Everlasting pea (g)					V				
Snapdragon (g)					V				
Misc. Shrubs (g)					V				
Buddleia							V	V	
Spear thistle						V			
Ragwort							V		
Buddleia (g)							V	V	
Ivy								V	
Ceanothus (g)									V
Pansy (g)									V

Worker	A	M	J	J	A	S
White deadnettle	V	V			P	P
Red deadnettle	V					
Wild rose		V				
White clover		V				
Comfrey		V	V			
Hoary plantain		P				
Dandelion		V				
Slender thistle		V				
Oil-seed rape (a)		V				
St John's wort			V			
Mallow			V	V		
Bramble			P	V		
Bird's-foot trefoil			V			
Tufted vetch			V			
Common vetch			V			
Fodder vetch			V			
White clover			V	V		
Red clover			V			
Black horehound			V	V		
Creeping thistle			V	V		
Aster (g)			V			
Hebe (g)			V			
Privet (g)			V			
Snowberry (g)			V			
Misc. Shrubs (g)			V			
Wild rose				V		
Goat's rue				V		
Restharrow				V		
Greater bindweed				V		
Greater burdock				V		
Spear thistle				V	V	
Misc. (g)				V		
Spiny restharrow					V	
Wild angelica					V	
Narrow-leaved bird's-foot trefoil						P
Ivy						P

behaviour was observed on various occasions, usually on areas of rough grassland, but also on the inner banks of sea walls, on a canal bank, under an old hedgerow, on an old, cracked wall, and on the bare earthen bank of a deep ditch. Queens were often noted exploring the bare earth under nettle beds, and among leaf litter below hawthorn scrub. In 1999 nest site prospecting by this species was observed through April and into the third week in May.

According to Sladen (1912) nests are usually underground, and approached by way of a long, downward-sloping tunnel. The comb is dark brown, untidy, and frequently covered by a wax-pollen canopy. Large quantities of pollen are stored, by workers, in tall wax cylinders. Again, according to Sladen, the colonies are tenaciously

Male	F	M	A	M	J	J	A	S	O
Rhododendron				V					
Red campion				V					
Mallow				V					
Bramble				V	V				
Common vetch				V					
Red clover				V					
Black horehound				V					
Marsh thistle				V					
Creeping thistle				V	V				
Hebe (g)				V					
Lavatera (g)				V		V			
Misc. Shrubs (g)				V					
Spear thistle					V	V			
Purple loosestrife						V			
Lesser burdock						V			
Knapweed						V			
Ragwort						V			
Devil's bit scabious							V		
Bristly oxtongue							V		
Dahlia (g)							V		
Lobelia (g)							V		
Ivy									V

Caste unspecified	F	M	A	M	J	J	A	S	O
Bird's-foot trefoil					V				
Hogweed					V				
Marsh thistle					V				
Sea lavender						V	V		
Purple loosestnfe						V			
Black horehound						V	V		
Greater knapweed						V			
Lavatera (g)						V			
Narrow-leaved bird's-foot trefoil							V		
Marsh woundwort							V		
Knapweed							V		
Golden samphire							V		
Hoary ragwort							V		

defended by the workers if disturbed. During the Essex survey, nests were detected on several occasions. One was observed in a hole on the inner bank of the sea wall at Tollesbury on 9/4/95. The hole was 2 cm in diameter and a *B. terrestris* queen was observed entering and leaving. Another nest, with numerous workers entering and leaving, was noted in a hole at the side of a concrete-surfaced cart track near Pleshey on 22/5/90. Workers were also observed entering and leaving a nest in a small hole in the soil on a wide, grassy ride in Hatfield Forest on 7/5/97. At Great Chesterford, on 19/5/92, a nest was observed in an ivy-covered church wall, about a metre above the ground.

Workers of this species begin to appear in late April or early May and continue foraging until mid or late September. The first males and young queens emerge in late May or early June and both may be observed through to early October. Fussell & Corbet (1992c) report several observations of males 'patrolling' along hedges and field boundaries on the Cambridge University Farm. A mating pair was observed at 12.45 p.m. on a footpath in Castle Park, Colchester on 13/9/98, the male looking very small perched on the hind segments of the queen's abdomen. As with *B. lucorum*, there is some evidence that young queens may establish summer colonies, rather than feed up prior to hibernation. On 25/6/99 a young queen was observed with full pollen loads on bramble flowers at Hilly Fields, Colchester. Fresh males were noted on ivy flowers at the same site as late as 7 and 8/10/99, and a young queen, also near Colchester, at garden flowers on 9/10/99. Perhaps significantly, the last-mentioned individual was noticeably smaller than average for queens of this species.

As with *B. lucorum*, there is evidence of prolonged seasonal activity, and possible over-wintering of colonies in the extreme south east of the county. Records supplied by D.G. Down of Thundersley indicate activity on the part of queens of this species throughout the autumn and winter in 1998 and 1999: 18/1, 2/2, 6/2, 9/2, 10/2, 15/2, 17/2, 26/2 and 7/10, 3/11, 29/11, 12/12 in 1998; 6/1, 21/1, 22/1, 21/2, 22/2, 23/2, 28/2 and 2/11, 7/11, 9/11 in 1999. Sometimes these winter-active bees were observed sunning themselves on warm days, in flight, or feeding from garden flowers including *Hebe*, winter-flowering *Lonicera*, *Mahonia*, *Erica* spp. and *Fuchsia*. Of particular interest is D.G. Down's frequent observation of queens inside crocus flowers as they opened in early morning, indicating that this is where they spent the nights.

Habitat and forage-sources

Like *B. lucorum*, this species occurs in a wide variety of habitats, including marginal uncultivated land on farms, roadside verges and remaining hedges, especially where these are bordered by ditches, woodland rides, river-banks, gardens, parks and public open spaces, and ruderal habitat associated with former industrial sites. In early spring queens are commonly observed prospecting for nest-sites along the inner banks of the sea walls, but such areas are poor in forage-sources at that time of year. By far the most frequently observed forage-source during this period (February to April) is sallow catkins (both male and female). They are also partial to blossom of blackthorn, cherry plum and gorse, as well as bluebells as they come into flower during April. These observations are to a degree at odds with Fussell & Corbet's (1991) view that hedgerows are more important for the herbaceous plants of the hedge-bottom than for the flowering shrubs (though they make an exception for bramble). This may be true during the latter part of the spring and summer, and for some species of *Bombus*, but during the early spring when very few herbaceous species are flowering, early-flowering shrubs play a very important role, especially for the short-tongued species such as *B. terrestris*. Bluebells, too, seem to be a significant nutritional source in spring for queens of this and several other species. This fact suggests that Williams's finding for Kent that 'densities of all bumble bees were found to be low inside closed-canopy woodlands, where flowers providing suitable food sources are usually sparse in summer' (Williams, 1988) might deserve some further comment. Williams's sampling took place between June 25 and July 25 to maximise the chances of recording all species present at his sites. However, if, as seems likely, availability of food sources in early spring is an important factor in the survival of queens and nest-establishment, then availability of early woodland-floor species such as bluebells may be more significant than observations made in summer might suggest. Although such woodlands may not by themselves sustain colonies through the year, this does not rule out their importance as part of a mosaic of habitat within the foraging range of such colonies, and exploited sequentially through the year.

As already indicated, queens of this species are frequently observed foraging from both herbaceous and woody garden flowers through the spring months. Young queens emerging from late May onwards feed on a range of hedgerow flowers (notably bramble, dogwood and mallow, and flowers of rough grassland, such as various thistles and ragworts). As in spring, they frequently visit parks and gardens, using a very wide range of cultivated herbs and shrubs as food sources. Workers, appearing from April onwards, are also very catholic in their forage-sources. In April they use white and red deadnettles, later diversifying to brambles, various Fabaceae (vetches, clovers and trefoils), comfreys, black horehound and various Asteraceae (thistles). Later in the year white deadnettle again becomes significant, along with ivy and late-flowering Fabaceae (bird's-foot trefoil and restharrows). Workers have been observed collecting pollen from the following flowers: bramble, narrow-leaved bird's-foot trefoil, hoary plantain, ivy and white deadnettle. Like the queens, they also frequent parks and gardens, where they visit a wide variety of herbs and shrubs, most notably *Hebe*, *Symphoricarpos* and *Ligustrum*. Males, appearing from late May onwards, visit a similarly wide variety of wild and cultivated plants. They are particularly associated with Asteraceae, such as thistles, knapweeds, bristly oxtongue and ragworts in mid to late summer; and ivy in autumn.

Distribution and status in Essex

Bombus terrestris is a 'Mainland Ubiquitous' species (Williams, 1982), which is widespread and common throughout Essex. Harwood (1884) included it in his Colchester list and Chapman (1962-66) regarded it as 'one of our commonest bumblebees'. During the post-1980 survey it has been recorded from 323 tetrads, spread across all 57 ten-kilometre squares in the county.

Chapter 6: Species Accounts   71

Bombus pratorum (Linnaeus)

Early-nesting bumblebee

This is a widespread and common
species throughout Essex.

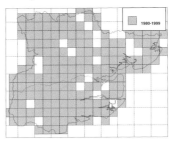

Description

Queens are usually somewhat
smaller than those of *B. terrestris*.
Their ground-colour is black,
with two bands of yellow, one on
the collar, the other on segment two of the abdomen. The tail is rust-red. However,
like several other *Bombus* species, there are melanic and semi-melanic colour forms.
Occasionally the yellow collar is reduced or broken in the middle as also is the
abdominal yellow band, which is occasionally absent (*e.g.* one at Colchester, 25/4/93).

Workers are very variable in size, some being very tiny indeed. Some resemble the
queens in colour-pattern, but more typically in Essex they entirely lack the yellow
abdominal band.

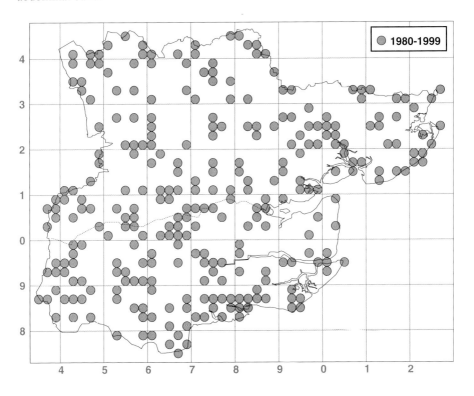

Males are quite distinctive. The yellow collar extends to the head and face, whilst the abdominal band is usually wider than in the females, although darker forms do occur much less commonly (in Essex). The tail is usually bright rust-red, but in older specimens this fades and almost white-tailed individuals can cause confusion.

Identification

The pattern of two yellow bands and a red tail is distinctive for the queens. During the summer, workers of *B. pratorum* which lack the yellow abdominal band could be confused with males of *B. lapidarius*. However, the yellow hairs on the face of the latter (black in *B. pratorum* workers) is usually a reliable guide for field identification. The bright, contrasting pattern of the males of this species is very distinctive.

Life-history

The English name, assigned to this species by Sladen (1912), is clearly appropriate, as workers of this species are frequently the first to appear in the spring (31/3/98) in most parts of the county. As this implies, the queens also emerge early from hibernation – usually at about the same time as *B. terrestris* queens. However, they generally establish their nests and produce the first brood of workers a little more quickly. This may explain why the queens of this species are more sporadically observed after emergence from hibernation than are the queens of *B. terrestris*, which are much more consistently in evidence at sallow blossom or prospecting for nest sites.

Queens of this species appear to be more flexible than most in their choice of nest sites. These may be underground (Sladen, 1912) but according to the survey conducted by Fussell & Corbet (1992a) they are more often at or above ground-level. They may be found in the roof spaces of buildings, bird boxes, and often in association with trees or shrubs. The nest reaches maturity relatively quickly, and the peak numbers of workers are smaller than is the case with *B. terrestris* and *B. lucorum*. Other authors (Sladen, 1912; Alford, 1975; Prŷs-Jones & Corbet, 1991) all concur in citing evidence that this species may be double-brooded. Evidence from recent years in Essex is suggestive of double, possibly even triple broods in some years. In 1997 queens were not observed until late March, and the first males and young queens were seen in the third week in May. However, no individuals of any caste were seen beyond the end of July. In 1998 the first workers were observed as early as the end of March, but males and young queens were not in evidence until the fourth week in May. However, there were sporadic sightings of all three castes during the last two weeks of August, suggesting the possibility of small second broods. In 1999, *B. pratorum* (like several other species) emerged rather late from hibernation, and the first workers were not observed until the fourth week in April. However, males and young queens were flying from mid May. Thereafter there were rather sporadic sightings of males and workers until late July. On 28/8 several workers were observed with pollen

This table excludes unusually early and late observations - see text

Queen	F	M	A	M	J	J	A
Sallow (m)	V	V					
Sallow (f)		V					
Ground ivy		V					
White deadnettle		P	V	V			
Berberis (g)		V					
Bergenia (g)		V					
Ceanothus (g)		V					
Flowering currant (g)		V					
Heathers (spp) (g)	V						
Blackthorn			V				
Red deadnettle			V				
Rosemary (g)			V				
Red campion				V			
Common vetch				V			
Cut-leaved cranesbill				V			
Bramble					V	V	
Bird's-foot trefoil					V		
Tufted vetch					V		
Comfrey					V		
Hound's tongue					V		
Self heal					V		
Marsh thistle					V		
Hawkweed					V		
Hebe (g)					V		
Red hot poker (g)					V		
Snowberry (g)					V		
Valerian (g)					V	V	
Misc. (g)					V		

Worker	F	M	A	M	J	J	A
Erica carnea (g)	V						
Green alkanet		V	V	V			
Bluebell(g)		V					
Ceanothus (g)		V	V				
Japonica (g)		V					
White deadnettle		V	V		V		
Mallow				V	V	V	
Bramble				P	V	V	
Wild rose				V		V	
Hawthorn				V			
Common vetch				V	V		
Broom				V			
Horse chestnut				V			
Sycamore				P			
Comfrey				V	V		
Cranesbill (g)				V			
Honeysuckle (g)				V			
Snowberry (g)				V	V		
Old Eng. Rose (g)				V			
Miscel. (g)				V	V	V	
Creeping buttercup					V		
Bird's-foot trefoil					V		
Tufted vetch					V		
Fodder vetch					V		
Bush vetch					V		
White clover					V	V	
Red clover					V		
Hound's tongue					V		
Black horehound					V	V	
Creeping thistle					V	V	
Hawkbit					V		
Bellflower (g)					V		
Hebe (g)					V		
Rhododendron (g)					V		
Valerian (g)					V		
Water figwort						V	
Spear thistle						V	
Knapweed						V	
Musk mallow							V
Purple loosestrife							V
Wild angelica							V
Red bartsia							P
Lavatera (g)							V

loads, foraging from red bartsia, near Copford, in north east Essex. Then, on 28/10 a queen was noted feeding from bramble at the Moors, Colchester. The pattern thus seems to be very variable from year to year, with indications of a small second brood in favourable years. It is open to speculation whether the single exceptionally late record of a foraging queen is consistent with an occasional third brood.

Male	F	M	A	M	J	J	A
Bramble				V	V	V	
White clover				V	V	V	
Comfrey				V	V		
Green alkanet				V	V		
White deadnettle				V			
Bugle				V			
Ground ivy				V			
Cranesbill (g)				V			
Foxglove (g)				V			
Perennial Cornflower(g)				V			
Rhododendron (g)				V	V		
Bush vetch					V		
Common vetch					V		
Hound's tongue					V		
Welted thistle					V		
Marsh thistle					V	V	
Creeping thistle					V		
Bellfiower (g)					V		
Cotoneaster (g)					V		
Hebe (g)					V		
Snapdragon (g)					V		
Snowberry (g)					V		
Valenan (g)					V		
Misc. (g)					V		
Spear thistle						V	
Hebe						V	
Lavender (g)						V	
Greater willowherb							V

Habitat and forage-sources

B. pratorum is another widespread species which may be found in a wide variety of habitats. It is particularly common in gardens, rough ground and public open spaces in urban areas. It also inhabits roadside verges, railway cuttings and agricultural set-aside, but appears to be generally less frequent in intensively farmed habitats than other common species such as *B. lucorum* and *B. terrestris*.

On emergence from hibernation the queens feed on sallow, white and red deadnettle, blackthorn and numerous species of cultivated herbaceous and woody plants. *Ribes sanguineum, Rosmarinus* and *Erica* spp. are particularly favoured.

In spring, workers of this species are particularly attracted to garden shrubs such as *Erica carnea, Chaenomeles* and *Ceanothus. Symphoricarpos, Lonicera, Rosa* spp. *Hebe, Valeriana* and many other cultivated species and varieties are also favoured, according to flowering season. Among the wild flowers, bramble blossom is particularly frequently visited for both nectar and pollen. Also noted as forage sources are mallows, wild rose, hawthorn, several species of Fabaceae (vetches, clovers, broom), comfrey, Lamiaceae (white deadnettle, black horehound) and Asteraceae (thistles, knapweed, hawkbit). In addition to bramble, red bartsia, white deadnettle, and sycamore were noted as pollen-sources.

Like queens and workers, the males of this species are particularly partial to garden flowers, including *Rhododendron, Digitalis, Hebe, Antirrhinum, Symphoricarpos, Campanula* and *Valeriana*. In uncultivated sites, bramble, mallow, green alkanet, comfrey, various Fabaceae (vetches and clovers), Lamiaceae (white deadnettle, bugle, ground ivy) and thistles are among the recorded forage-sources.

Distribution

This is another 'Mainland Ubiquitous' species, which is common and widespread throughout Essex. It is a little less frequently observed than other common species, but this may be due to the smaller size of mature colonies. During the present survey, *B. pratorum* was recorded from 284 tetrads in all 57 ten-kilometre squares in the county. My subjective impressions are that this species is increasingly urban and adapts less well to agricultural intensification than do some of the other common species. Unless private gardens and public open spaces meet all its ecological requirements, continued development of so-called 'brown-field' sites may result in serious declines of this bee in the future.

Bombus lapidarius (Linnaeus)

Red-tailed bumblebee

This is another common and widespread species in Essex, though with significant seasonal fluctuations.

Description

Queens are large, and mainly black, with a red tail. The hairs on the thorax and abdomen are relatively short and even, giving a rather velvety appearance (especially when they are freshly emerged). The sting sheath is as in fig. 5.31a.

Workers are similarly coloured, but smaller – sometimes very tiny indeed.

Males are quite variable in coloration. The most common form in Essex is black with a single yellow band on the collar, a tuft of yellow hairs on the face, and a reddish tail. Often there are yellow hairs mixed in with the black on the scutellum but these do

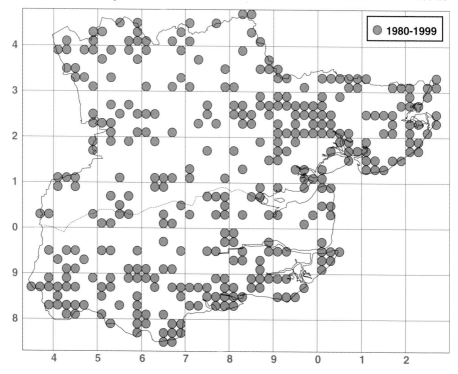

not form a clearly distinct band. Individuals may show varying degrees of darkening, with the yellow collar significantly reduced. In such specimens, the tail is often a dull yellow/orange. As with *B. pratorum*, the colours of *B. lapidarius* males are liable to fade with age.

Identification

Females of both castes are likely to be confused with only one other species in Essex. This is the more localised *B. ruderarius*. The queens of the latter species are usually significantly smaller than those of *B. lapidarius*. Typically the red of the tail is more rusty than that of *B. lapidarius*, and the black coat is dull and sooty, rather than velvet-black. However, these are unreliable characters, and a clearer feature for field identification is the red corbicular hairs in *B. ruderarius* (black in *B. lapidarius*). In Essex, at least, this seems to be a reliable character, and is surprisingly evident in the field. For critical identification of captured specimens the following features are helpful: inner projections of sting sheath wide in *B. ruderarius*, much narrower in *B lapidarius* (fig. 5.31a & b); mid-basitarsus of *B. lapidarius* without spine, *B. ruderarius* with spine (fig. 5.13).

Workers are much less easy to distinguish from those of *B. ruderarius*, since in the latter species the corbicular hairs are often partly black, whilst in *B. lapidarius* workers they tend to fade with age, and may be discoloured by pollen grains. Even with captured specimens, the distinctive feature of the sting-sheath is not easy to make out, especially with very small individuals.

Males can be confused with workers of *B. pratorum* but the yellow hairs on the face in male *B. lapidarius* are distinctive. More difficult is the separation of *B. lapidarius* and *B. ruderarius* males in the field. Pale forms of *B. ruderarius* often have an indistinct yellow band on the front of the abdomen, as well as a yellow band on the scutellum. However, dark forms of *B. ruderarius* males look very similar to *B. lapidarius* and microscopic examination may be necessary for critical determination. The genital capsules are quite distinct (see fig. 5.32 a & d).

Life-history

Queens of this species emerge from hibernation during March (though D.G. Down reports sightings of two queens of this species on 13/2/98, in his garden at Thundersley), often as much as three to four weeks later than *B. terrestris* or *B. pratorum*. Females may be observed searching for nest-sites through April and into mid May. According to Sladen (1912) '*The usual position of the nest is under the ground and the tunnel is generally from 18 inches to 2 feet long, but sometimes it extends to 3 feet, and in one nest I dug up it was over 7 feet. I have never found an unsheltered nest on the ground, but a favourite place is in the walls of barns and outhouses, often at considerable height above ground. The name of* lapidarius *was given to this species on account of its habit of nesting under large stones...'.* The survey conducted by Fussell & Corbet (1992a) confirmed that nest-sites used by this species are generally underground. Also, they were reported to nest more frequently than other species in soil close to brick, concrete, stone or bare earth. *B. lapidarius* has a higher temperature threshold for activity than other common species, and Fussell & Corbet consider that they may benefit from heat-reservoir effects in their chosen nest locations. This fact may also account for the generally later emergence from hibernation of queens of this species, and also their greater tendency to sunbathe in early spring sunshine. In Essex observations of both nest-site prospecting activity by queens, and of actual nest-sites all indicated below-ground sites, usually in holes in ditch-banks, woodland edge, grassland or (commonly) on inner banks of sea walls. Several chosen sites were holes in bare earth, one (23/6/93, near Cheshunt) was in a hole 1.2–2 cm in diameter in soil below mowed turf, another on a west-facing grassy bank near Audley End station (12/5/93). Sladen (1912) states that the comb is particularly neat and clean, and that wax is produced in great quantities. The comb is usually covered by a wax-pollen canopy.

The first workers are seen from mid to late May, but their numbers build very slowly to a peak in July and August. Young queens are usually first seen in late June, as are the males. However, in 1997 a few males were seen in the third week in May, possibly the offspring of unfertilised eggs laid by workers. On 7/6/98 a young queen was observed apparently nest-site prospecting on a south-facing bank at the edge of a suburban garden (at Ingatestone). This, together with exceptionally late sightings of queen *B. lapidarius* at Frinton-on-Sea on 13/10/97 (T.B.) and at Westcliff, Southend on 7/11/99 (R.G.P.) are the only evidence which might point to double broods in this species. In general, colonies are in decline by the end of August, with some individual workers and males continuing to forage into early or mid September. Fussell & Corbet (1992c) describe several instances of patrolling by numbers of males along field boundaries or grassland (in Kent, also along sea walls; P. Williams, pers. comm.). They visit high points along their routes but are not restricted to areas of tall vegetation. A male *B. lapidarius* was observed mating with a young queen *B. lucorum* as she nectared at bramble near Maldon, on 17/7/94. More conventionally, a pair of copulating *B. lapidarius* was observed (see plate 11) on the tow path of the Stort south of Bishop's Stortford on 18/7/98. Queens typically hibernate in woodlands (M. Edwards, pers. comm.).

Habitat and forage-sources

Like other common species, *B. lapidarius* is found in a wide range of both cultivated and uncultivated habitat: gardens, public parks and open spaces, open woodland, golf courses, coastal marshes and hedgerows. After hibernation queens spend a

Queen	M	A	M	J	J	A
Lesser celandine	V					
Sallow (m & f)	V	V				
Red deadnettle	V	V	V			
Heathers (g)	V					
Scabious (g)	V					
Crocus (g)		V				
Ribes (g)		V				
Blackthorn		V				
Gorse		V				
Crab apple		V	V			
White deadnettle		V	V			
Bluebell		V	V			
Oil-seed rape (a)		V	V			
Common vetch			V	V		
Green alkanet			V			
Rose (g)			V			
Misc. (g)			V			
Field bean (a)			V			
Mallow				V	V	
Bramble				V		
Medick				V		
Thistles				V		
Hebe (g)				V	V	V
Purple loosestrife					V	
Large bindweed					V	
Lesser burdock					V	V
Spear thistle					V	V
Greater knapweed					V	
Knapweed					V	
Marjoram						V
Busy Lizzy (g)						V
Lavatera (g)						V

Worker	A	M	J	J	A	S
Buttercup	V					
Bird's-foot trefoil	V	V	V	V		
Green alkanet	V	V				
Laburnum (g)	V					
Mallow		V	V			
Bramble		V	V			
Creeping cinquefoil		P	V			
Narrow-leaved bird's-foot trefoil		V	V	V	V	
Tufted vetch		V	V			
Tare		V				
Grass vetchling		V				
Melilot		V	V			
Sea clover		V				
White clover		V	V	V	V	
Tree lupin		P				
Comfrey		V				
Slender thistle		V				
Marsh thistle		V	V			
Creeping thistle		V	V	V		
Cat's-ears		V				
Dandelion		V				
Hawkweed		V				
Aster (g)		V				
Hebe (g)		V	V			
Misc. (g)		V	V			
Sea lavender				V		
Restharrow				V		
Red clover				V		
Greater bindweed				V		
Black horehound				V		
Spear thistle				V	V	
Knapweed				V	V	V
Bristly oxtongue				V		
Lavatera (g)				V		
Spiny restharrow					V	
Golden samphire					V	
Ragwort					V	
Hoary ragwort					V	
Rosebay willowherb						V

considerable time apparently grounded in cool weather, or sunning themselves when conditions permit. At this time of year they forage from such wild flowers as sallow catkins, red and white deadnettles, blackthorn and gorse, and various garden flowers as well as field bean and rape as they come into flower. They are also commonly found along with *B. terrestris* at woodland bluebells in April and May. Later in the year, the young queens also feed on a variety of garden flowers (*Hebe, Lavatera, Impatiens* and others) as well as wild species, most notably mallow, bramble, purple

Male	M	A	M	J	J	A
Mallow				V	V	V
Bramble				V	V	V
Creeping thistle				V		
Hebe (g)				V	V	V
Privet (g)				V		
Melilot					V	
White clover					V	
Large bindweed					V	
Lesser burdock					V	V
Spear thistle					V	V
Marsh thistle					V	V
Creeping thistle					V	V
Knapweed					V	V
L.avatera (g)					V	V
Bird's-foot trefoil						V
Purple loosestrife						V
Greater willowherb						V
Black horehound						V
Marjoram						V
Water mint						V
Field scabious						V
Devil's-bit scabious						V
Ragwort						V
Hoary ragwort						V
Dahlia (g)						V

loosestrife, lesser burdock, various thistles and knapweed.

Workers also forage from a wide range of both wild and cultivated flowers, including buttercup, green alkanet, *Laburnum*, *Lavatera*, *Hebe*, *Aster*, rosebay willowherb and many more. However, they are most commonly observed at mallow and numerous species of low-growing flowers in 'brown-field' sites, lawns, rabbit-grazed or mown grassland. Various Fabaceae are especially favoured: narrow-leaved and common bird's-foot trefoil, tufted vetch, grass vetchling, melilot, rest-harrows, white, red and sea clovers and tree lupin. Tree lupin and creeping cinquefoil have been noted as pollen sources. Workers observed foraging from an extensive patch of the latter flower along the margins of the station car-park at Newport, Essex performed a rapid twirl on each flower before moving on to the next. They periodically stopped to scrape pollen onto their corbicula. It seems likely that the twirl functions (similarly to buzz-foraging) to release pollen from the anthers of flowers such as cinquefoil which have open, symmetrical corollae. The flowers of the Fabaceae, more commonly visited by *B. lapidarius* workers, are zygomorphic and so structured as to ensure that pollen is released by insects in the course of probing the flowers for nectar. Workers of this species are particularly evident foraging on the bird's-foot trefoils, clovers and spiny restharrow on remaining coastal grazing marshes and by the sea walls. In such habitats they are sometimes accompanied by workers of the much rarer *B. muscorum*.

Males are commonly seen through June, July and August on mallow, bramble, melilot, purple loosestrife and a range of garden flowers (*Hebe* and *Lavatera*, especially). However, they are most abundant on flower-heads of Asteraceae such as lesser burdock, various thistles, knapweed, and ragworts as well as field and devil's-bit scabious and various Lamiaceae (black horehound, water mint and marjoram).

Distribution and status in Essex

Considered one of the 'Mainland Ubiquitous' species, *B. lapidarius* is less common in the north but apparently spreading in Scotland. Harwood (1884) included it in his Colchester list and Chapman (1962-66) gave various records spanning the intervening period and declared it 'one of our more common bumblebees'. It is widespread and common, having been recorded from 344 tetrads in all 57 ten-kilometre squares in the county during the present survey.

Bombus hortorum (Linnaeus)

Garden bumblebee

Widespread and fairly common throughout Essex, but more localised than the other common species.

Description

Queens are medium-sized. The ground colour of the coat is black, with a yellow band on the collar, another, narrower one on the scutellum, and a third on the first and second segments of the abdomen. The tail is white. In typical specimens, the yellow is bright, similar in hue to the yellow bands on *B. lucorum*. However, in some specimens the band on the abdomen may be reduced, and broken in the middle. There is a rare melanic form in which the yellow bands are more-or-less absent, and the tail is black. I have not so far encountered this form in Essex.

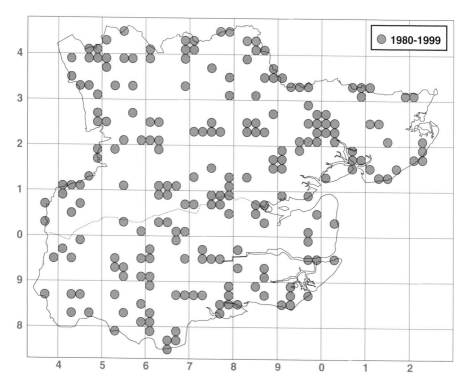

Queen	M	A	M	J	J	A
White deadnettle	V	P	V			
Dandelion	V					
Narcissus (g)	V					
Heathers (g)	V	V				
Ground ivy		V	V			
Red deadnettle		V				
Bluebell		V	V			
Aubrieta (g)		V				
Tufted vetch			V			V
Common vetch			V	V		
Comfrey			V	V		
Snapdragon (g)			V			
Field bean (a)			V			
Bramble				V		
White clover				V		
Black horehound				V		
Yellow iris (g)				V		
Misc. (g)				V		
Teasel						V
Spear thistle						V

Worker	A	M	J	J	A	S
White deadnettle	P	V	V	V		
Common vetch		V				
Red clover		V	V		V	
Bugle		V				
Ground ivy		P	V			
Honeysuckle (g)		V	V			
Comfrey		V	V			
Red campion			V			
Bramble			V	V		
Tufted vetch			V	V		
Bush vetch			V			
Zig-zag clover			V			
Black horehound			V	V	V	V
Common toadflax			V			
Foxglove			V			
Everlasting pea (g)			V			
Foxglove (g)			P			
Lavender (g)			V			
Purple toadflax (g)			V			
Privet (g)			V			
Sage (g)			V			
Field bean (a)			V			
Greater bindweed				V		
Hedge woundwort				V		
Spear thistle				V	V	
Marsh thistle				V		
Buddleia (g)				V		
Red bartsia					V	

The face is markedly elongated, a feature which immediately distinguishes this from all other common species (see fig. 5.17a, and plate 17). The coat is relatively long and uneven.

Workers are variable in size, the larger ones overlapping the smaller queens. Their colour-pattern is the same as that of the queens, though they are more liable to some degree of darkening and reduction of the yellow bands, especially that on the abdomen.

Males also are similar in colour pattern. The rounded tip to the abdomen and extra antennal segment can be used to confirm the sex of individual specimens on close examination. Darkened forms, in which the thoracic yellow bands are greatly reduced and the abdominal one more-or-less absent, are relatively common in Essex. Fully melanic forms are occasionally met with (*e.g.* 23/6/93, Hunsdon Mead; 3/6/97, suburban garden, Chingford).

Identification

The pattern of black ground colour with three yellow bands, a white tail, and long face distinguish all castes from other common species. Melanic forms require closer

Male	M	A	M	J	J	A
Red campion			V	V		
White deadnettle			V			
Mallow				V		
Bramble				V		
Common vetch				V		
Comfrey				V		
Hedge woundwort				V	V	
Black horehound				V		
Foxglove				V		
Spear thistle					V	
Lavender (g)					V	
Teasel					V	
Knapweed						V

examination, but the long face is diagnostic. Confusion with two other species is possible. *B. ruderatus* is very rare indeed, but is very occasionally seen in Essex. The queens of *B. ruderatus* can be distinguished from those of *B. hortorum* by their (usually) larger size and generally robust appearance. The yellow bands are somewhat darker than in *B. hortorum*, the coat is shorter and more even, the bands on the collar and scutellum are approximately equal in width at the middle (that on the scutellum narrower in *B. hortorum*), and the sculpturing on the dorsal surface of the final segment of the abdomen more coarse in *B. ruderatus* (fig. 5.20 a & b). The Essex specimens of *B. ruderatus* I have examined are darkened, with the abdominal band confined to the first segment and broken in the middle, or entirely absent. The yellow bands on the thorax are very narrow. How far these features serve to distinguish workers of the two species is unclear: I have no confirmed examples of workers of *B. ruderatus* from Essex during the survey period. Males of *B. ruderatus* have a wider and more clearly demarcated yellow band on the scutellum than do those of *B. hortorum*, and the 'beard' on the mandibles of *B. ruderatus* is reddish, black in *B. hortorum*. These differences in colour pattern are useful for field identification, but more detailed examination is required for definitive identification. The length and distribution of the hairs on the hind tibia are distinctive (see fig. 5.23 a & b).

B. jonellus is another species with which *B. hortorum* could be confused. It too has a pattern of three yellow bands and a white tail. This species has been recorded only once in Essex so far, but may well have been overlooked. It can be readily distinguished from *B. hortorum* by its much shorter face. With microscopic examination, there are differences in the female mandibles (fig. 5.18 a & b) and mid-basitarsi (fig. 5.19 a & b). The male genital capsules are markedly different (fig. 5.32 b & i).

Life-history

The first queens may be observed from late March onwards. They appear to establish their nests soon after emerging from hibernation (queen with pollen loads noted on 7/4/99 at Colchester), though nesting behaviour was rarely observed during the survey. Sladen (1912) states that the nests of this species are generally underground, with a short entrance tunnel, though he reports finding one in a sparrow's nest about twenty feet above the ground in Virginia creeper. Fussell & Corbet (1992a) report from the survey they organised that only about half of *B. hortorum* nests were below ground, and that they were commonly in situations exposed to sunlight. According to Sladen, relatively few workers ('seldom...more than 100 workers') are produced in each nest. In Essex, the first workers are usually in evidence from late April, but in some years foraging queens may be seen as late as the third week in May (*e.g.* 16/5/99, on *Antirrhinum*, with pollen loads, Colchester). Young females and males appear from late May onwards (no males observed until July in 1999). Darwin (n.d.) made a brilliant series of observations on the male 'patrolling' behaviour in his garden. Males followed a regular route, stopping at 'buzzing places' as they did so. He observed this from the middle of July to the end of September and over several years. The constancy of the behaviour was established by an unusual experimental procedure: '*The flight paths remain the same for a considerable time, and buzzing places are fixed within an inch. I was able to prove this by stationing five or six of my children, on a number of separate occasions, each close to a buzzing place, and telling the one farthest away to shout out "here is a bee" as soon as one was buzzing around. The others followed this up, so that the same cry of "here is a bee" was passed on from child to child without interruption until the bees reached the buzzing place where I myself was standing.*'

Colonies continue to be active until late July or early August (occasionally as late as the beginning of September). According to Prŷs-Jones & Corbet (1991) *B. hortorum* has a short life-cycle, with evidence of second broods. Sladen (1912) also speculates that a nest he examined on 17/7/1911 had been established by a queen reared that season. There is little evidence of second broods in the Essex survey, except, possibly, an exceptionally late record of a queen of this species nectaring on white deadnettle on 26/10/95 near Colne Engaine.

Habitat and forage-sources

B. hortorum is a long-tongued species which forages mainly from flowers with long corolla-tubes, including, as its vernacular name implies, many garden varieties. It may be found in urban parks, private gardens, public open spaces in urban areas, roadside verges and hedgerows, and marginal habitat in farmland.

After hibernation, queens feed predominantly on white deadnettle (an important pollen-source), but will also visit other Lamiaceae such as red deadnettle and ground ivy. Bluebells, comfrey and various Fabaceae are also visited as they come into flower. Early garden flowers visted by hibernated queens include species with long corolla-tubes such as *Narcissus* and *Aubrieta*. Later in the year, freshly emerged queens visit vetches and clovers as well as black horehound, comfrey, teasel, various thistles and garden flowers such as snapdragon and honeysuckle.

Like the queens, workers are particularly frequent on white deadnettle, a regular forage-source from April through to July. Other Lamiaceae are also popular, including bugle, ground ivy (also a recorded pollen source), black horehound and hedge woundwort. Also commonly visited are various Fabaceae (bush and tufted vetches, red and zig-zag clover) and red bartsia. The latter flower is significant for surviving colonies during August and early September, along with black horehound and various thistles. Among garden flowers *Lonicera* (but possibly not all cultivars) is particularly attractive – so much so that during my survey work I learned to 'hang around' gardens with honeysuckle to await the arrival of *B. hortorum* workers (doing this while trying to look like an innocent passer-by is not as easy as you might think!). Foxgloves in both woods and gardens are also commonly visited; the bees completely disappear into the long corolla tubes, and subsequently leave (usually covered in pollen) rear-end first.

The males, at their numerical peak in June and early July, visit a similar range of Lamiaceae and Fabaceae, and are also very partial to foxglove and comfrey. However, they also visit flowers with open corollae, such as mallow and bramble. Teasels, thistles and knapweed are also visited in July and August.

A study by Fussell & Corbet (1991) carried out on farmland in Cambridgeshire showed this species to be a significant visitor to field bean. However, they point out that crops are transient sources of nutrition for the bees, which require supplies of pollen and nectar throughout their flight-period. So, for agricultural crops to benefit, it is necessary that uncultivated field-corners, hedges and ditches, grassy banks and so on are retained to provide suitable habitat throughout the year. In particular, they argue the importance of *permanent* semi-natural habitat, to sustain perennial herbaceous plants (such as white deadnettle, hedge woundwort and black horehound) which have the greatest nutritional value. Transient set-aside, which may be of benefit to some common butterflies, is of much less value for *Bombus* species. Their list of forage plants used by this species tallies very closely with observations of agricultural habitats in Essex, especially with regard to the importance of the common Lamiaceae throughout the flight-period.

Distribution and status in Essex

B. hortorum is a 'Mainland Ubiquitous' species, being widespread through England, Wales and north through Scotland and the Isles. Because this species has a shorter season than other common species, and also a relatively small number of workers per nest, it is probably somewhat under-recorded in the Essex survey. However, it was recorded from 213 tetrads in all 57 ten-kilometre squares in the county.

Bombus jonellus (Kirby)

This is a 'Widespread Local' species in Britain (Williams 1982), but there were no reliable records of it in Essex prior to its discovery on 19/06/00, just as this book was going to press.

Description

Queens are generally somewhat smaller than those of *B. hortorum*, which they closely resemble. The face is black, with yellow hairs on the top of the head. The thorax is black, with yellow bands on the collar and scutellum. The abdomen is black with a yellow band on segment one, sometimes also on segment two, and the tail is white. The face is short (length and width about equal), and the hairs on the corbicula usually ginger-red in colour.

Workers are similar, but smaller.

Males are similarly coloured, but have yellow hairs on the face.

Identification

Confusion with *B. ruderatus* and *B. subterraneus* is possible, but, given the extreme rarity of these species in Essex, unlikely. The short face of *B. jonellus* is the most obvious character for distinguishing *B. jonellus* from these two species, as well as separating it from the very similar *B. hortorum*. This is a good 'field' character, as are the ginger-red corbicular hairs, and, in the males, the yellow face. Females of *B. jonellus* have a notch but no oblique groove on the mandibles (no notch, but an oblique groove in *B. hortorum*) and no spine on the mid basitarsus (spine in *B. hortorum*). See the key in chapter 5, figures 5.18 and 5.19. The male genital capsule is very different from *B. hortorum* (and both *B. ruderatus* and *B. subterraneus*): note the sagittae taper to inwardly directed 'hooks' (similar to *B. pratorum*). See figure 5.32i.

Life-history

There appears to be relatively little published information. Sladen reports finding a nest of the species in a squirrel's nest at the top of a 'Scotch fir' (Sladen 1912). Alford (1975) cites Fraser (1949) for a record of a colony in a fallen birds' nest, and suggests that its biology is probably similar to that of *B. pratorum* (to which it is closely related). Williams (1989) observed it at Dungeness, but did not confirm it as successfully breeding in his survey area. However, a queen (or queens?) was found dead in a nest of *B. sylvarum*, indicating, at least, that queens did search for nest sites in his survey area. In Williams's survey, workers were seen from late April to the end of August, and queens from the second week in July to the end of July. This does seem to suggest that *B. jonellus*, like *B. pratorum*, nests early in the season.

So far, a single queen of this species is the only confirmed Essex record. This appeared to be in fresh condition when observed on 19/06/00, and so is likely to have been a young queen. However, despite extensive searching, no workers or males were found at the site.

Habitat and forage-sources

B. jonellus is reputed to be closely associated with heathland and moorland, but also coastal habitats. Alford (1975) gives broom, bramble, bilberry and other members of the Ericaceae as favoured forage-plants. The specimen observed in Essex was feeding systematically on heads of white clover on old grazing marsh on the RSPB reserve at Old Hall Marsh. Other flowering plants in the vicinity included bird's-foot trefoil, red clover and common vetch. No pollen collection was observed

Distribution and status in Essex

In Britain, this species has a northerly and westerly distribution, with further concentrations in the south-east (Surrey, east Sussex and east Kent), and East Anglia (Norfolk). Williams (1989b) includes this species in his 'Widespread Local' category. However, owing to the ease with which it may be confused with *B. hortorum*, it may well have been overlooked in some areas.

The species is not mentioned in Harwood's 1884 list for the Colchester area. Morley (1899) reports 'workers abundant on the purple heath at Lowestoft', and Sladen (1912) declared it 'rare in East Kent'. It was searched for on remaining areas of heather heath in Epping Forest during the present survey period by Mark Hanson and myself, but without success. No Essex records were included in the IBRA/ITE *Atlas*.

The very recent discovery of a single queen on Old Hall Marsh nature reserve poses interesting questions. If, as seems likely, this was a newly emerged young queen, the species is probably breeding at this locality. There are other extensive areas of grazing marsh in the vicinity, and it is possible that the species occurs at low density on these, too, but has so far been overlooked.

Plate 1 (above) *Bombus lucorum* male (pale form)

Plate 2 (right) *B. lucorom* worker captured by a crab spider

Plate 3 (below, right) *B. lucorum* queen (workers are similar)

Plate 4 (below) *B. lucorum* male

Note: all the colour plates are from photographs by the author. All insects were photographed in the wild, in Essex, unless otherwise stated.

Plate 5 (top, left) *Bombus terrestris* male

Plate 6 (top) *B. terrestris* fresh queen

Plate 7 (above) *B. terrestris* worker

Plate 8 (left) *Bombus pratorum* over-wintered queen

Plate 9 (below, left) *B. pratorum* male

Plate 10 (below) *B. pratorum* worker 'robbing' comfrey

Plate 11 (above, top) *Bombus lapidarius* mating pair

Plate 12 (above) *Bombus lapidarius* male (dark form)

Plate 13 (top, right) *B. lapidarius* male, pale form

Plate 14 (below, right) *B. lapidarius* queen

Plate 15 (below) *B. lapidarius* fresh queen with mites on thorax

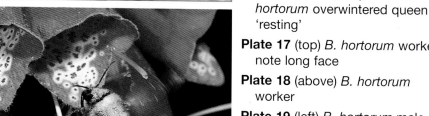

Plate 16 (above, left) *Bombus hortorum* overwintered queen 'resting'

Plate 17 (top) *B. hortorum* worker, note long face

Plate 18 (above) *B. hortorum* worker

Plate 19 (left) *B. hortorum* male

Plate 20 (below, left) *Bombus jonellus* queen

Plate 21 (below) *B. jonellus* queen, note short face

Plate 22 (above) *Bombus pascuorum* worker with pollen load

Plate 23 (right) *B. pascuorum* queen

Plate 24 (below) *B. pascuorum* over-wintered queen 'sunbathing'

Plate 25 (bottom) *B. pascuorum* male

Plate 26 (below, right) *Bombus ruderatuts* queen (in captivity)

Plate 27 (above) *Bombus humilis* over-wintered queen

Plate 28 (left) *B. humilis* worker with pollen load

Plate 29 (below) *B. humilis* male

Plate 30 (above) *Bombus muscorum* worker

Plate 31 (right) *B. muscorum* worker

Plate 32 (below, right) *B. muscorum* male

Plate 33 (below) *B. muscorum* worker

Note: queens are similar to workers

Plate 34 (above, left)
Bombus ruderarius
male

Plate 35 (above)
B. ruderarius worker

Plate 36 (left)
B. ruderarius male

Plate 37 (below)
B. ruderarius 'grounded'
queen

Plate 38 (above) *Bombus sylvarum* over-wintered green

Plate 39 (right) *B. sylvarum* queen

Plate 40 (below) *B. sylvarum* male

Plate 41 (right, below) *B. sylvarum* worker

Plate 42 (bottom) *B. sylvarum* queen

Plate 43 (bottom, right) *B. sylvarum* male

Plate 44 (top, left) *Bombus (Psithyrus) vestalis* male

Plate 45 (above) *B. (P.) vestalis* female

Plate 46 (left) *B. (P.) rupestris* male

Plate 47 (below, left) *Bombus (Psithyrus) rupestris* female (photographed in France

Plate 48 (below) *Bombus (Psithyrus) barbutellus* male

Plate 49 (bottom, left)
   B. (P.) barbutellus female

Plate 50 (mid, left)
   Bombus (P.) campestris
   female

Plate 51 (right)
   B. (P.) campestris male

Plate 52 (mid, right)
   B. (P.) campestris
   female

Plate 53 (bottom, right)
   B. (P.) campestris
   male, black form

Plate 54 (top, left) *B. (P.) sylvestris* over-wintered female

Plate 55 (left) *Bombus (Psithyrus) sylvestris* male: note ginger tip of abdomen

Plate 56 (above) Solitary bee *Anthophora plumipes* which resembles *B. lapidarius*

Plate 57 (below, left) Broad-bordered bee hawkmoth (photo in Hampshire)

Plate 58 (below) *Bombylius major:* a beefly which resembles *B. pascuarum*

Plate 59 (above) *Eristalis intricarius:* a hoverfly 'mimic' of *B. lapidarius*

Plate 60 (above, right) *Merodon equestris:* a hoverfly 'mimic' of *B. pratorum*

Plate 61 (right) *Volucella bombylans* form which 'mimics' *B. lapidarius*

Plate 62 (below) *Volucella bombylans* form which 'mimics' *B. hortorum*

Plate 63 (above) Suburban garden in Colchester; a habitat for all the common bumblebee species

Plate 64 (below) Hilly Fields, Colchester, habitat of eleven species of bumblebees

Plate 65 (above) Old Hall Marsh, habitat of *B. jonellus* and *B. muscorum*. Note the abundant clovers

Plate 66 (below) Arable landscape in north-west Essex: one reason for the decline of bumblebees

Plate 67 (above) Canvey Island: habitat of *B.sylvarum* and *B. muscorum* in spring. Note the fodder vetch

Plate 68 (below) Canvey Island in late summer. Note the abundant bird's-foot trefoil. Now a 'brown field' development site

Bombus ruderatus (Fabricius)

This is now one of the rarest British bumblebees, and has been recorded only very occasionally in Essex in recent years. The national distribution map is especially misleading as to its current status, and is a guide to its past range only.

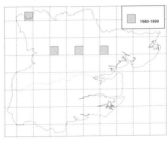

Description

Queens are usually very large, comparable in size with queens of *B. terrestris* and *B. lapidarius*. In general appearance they resemble large, dark *B. hortorum* queens. However, the yellow bands on the thorax are less bright, and usually narrower than in the typical forms of the latter. The width of the band on the collar is approximately equal to that on the hind margin of the thorax. The yellow band on the abdomen is confined to the first dorsal segment, and is commonly broken in the middle, or entirely absent. The tail is rather dull and off-white in the specimens I have seen. The coat is

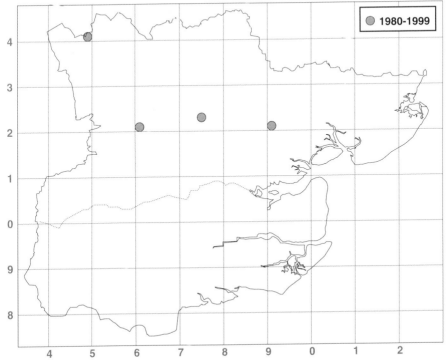

short and even; like *B. hortorum* the face is long and narrow.

Workers are similar to the queens, though smaller.

Males have a similar pattern of three yellow bands and a whitish tail, but the yellow is more extensive than in the (commoner) darkened forms of the queen. The yellow band at the rear of the thorax is as wide or wider at its mid line than the collar, and is clearly demarcated from the black band between them. This form of the male usually has a reddish beard on the mandibles. Entirely black forms of the male occur, but have not been met with in this study. Alford (1975) figures a black male (ab. *harrisellus*) from Essex, but no further details are available.

Identification

Paler forms of this species may be confused with *B. hortorum*. Distinction between *B. hortorum* and *B. ruderatus* is dealt with in the account of the former species. Darker forms of *B. ruderatus*, lacking the abdominal yellow band, are very similar to *B. subterraneus*. Although the latter species is now considered extinct in Britain, it formerly occurred in Essex. Queens of *B. subterraneus* have a clearly defined keel along the mid-line of the final ventral plate of the abdomen (fig. 5.21), whilst this plate may be angled along the mid-line in *B. ruderatus*, but not keeled. Males of *B. subterraneus* are more obviously different from *B. ruderatus*, having mainly yellowish hair on the abdomen and a short face.

Life-history

This species was so rarely observed during the present survey, that few inferences can be made about its phenology in the county. Saunders (1896) states that it nests underground, often in the old burrows of small mammals. Sladen also reports it as nesting underground, often with a long entrance-hole, but admits to having 'very seldom' found nests of this species (Sladen, 1912). The queens are said to emerge from hibernation later than those of *B. hortorum*, their colonies are more prolific, and break up later in the year. Falk (1991) says that the 'queens hibernate, probably in tunnels excavated in banks, slopes, etc., and emerge from April onwards'. Studies in Kent found that queens emerge from hibernation from mid May onwards, workers appear from mid June, and the males from the second week of July (Williams, 1989a).

Sladen (1912) states that the males follow one another, flying high among the foliage of selected trees. Williams (pers. comm.) notes that, at Dungeness, the males flew over low broom vegetation, with apparently typical patrolling behaviour.

Habitat and forage-sources

Like *B. hortorum, B. ruderatus* is a long-tongued species that visits flowers with corolla-tubes. Sladen (1912) reports that its 'special favourites are the white dead-nettle, horehound, and red clover'. Alford (1975) adds woundworts and Falk (citing Williams) adds toadflax. Comfrey, white clover, broad beans, motherwort and rosebay willowherb are also mentioned in the literature (Edwards, 1998). In Essex, one male was observed foraging from sulphur clover at one of the very few remaining areas of chalk grassland in the county (Dunmow railway cutting), and a queen was observed foraging from tubs of *Petunia* and *Impatiens* outside a village pub on 28/8/99! In Kent the habitat was well-drained open areas not subject to frequent drastic disturbance (Williams, 1988). Spring queens foraged from foxglove, and in summer workers foraged from viper's bugloss, toadflax, teasel and wood sage (Williams, 1989a).

Distribution and status in Essex

Sladen (1912) reported the species 'very common' in England, though less abundant in Scotland. Alford (1975) states that it does not occur in Scotland at all, and has suffered a decline in England so that 'at the present time,...*ruderatus*, though not necessarily rare, must be regarded as one of our less common species'. *The Atlas of the Bumblebees of the British Isles* (IBRA/ITE, 1980) gives a post-1960 (latest records from 1976) distribution almost wholly confined to south and south-east England, in fewer than 90 ten-kilometre squares. Unfortunately there is considerable doubt about the accuracy of some of the records plotted on these maps, especially in the case of *B. ruderatus.* Nevertheless, the general picture of rapid decline, accentuated in subsequent years is not in doubt. Falk (1991, citing Williams, 1982 and 1986) refers to it as 'a very local and declined species'. Archer (1998) classifies it as 'scarce', and alarm about its decline was sufficient for its inclusion (on the 'middle list') among only five *Bombus* species regarded as 'Globally Threatened/Declining' in the UK Biodiversity Steering Group's Report (1995). A 'Bumblebee Working Group' was subsequently established under the leadership of the WWF. Despite extensive surveying by this group in 1997 to 1999 only one male of *B. ruderatus* was observed in one site (Dungeness, in Kent) plus what may have been another near Salisbury Plain (Edwards, 1999).

In Essex, the species was collected by W.H. Harwood in the vicinity of Colchester (Harwood, 1884) and there is a specimen from St Osyth in 1893. The Natural History Museum (London) collection contains melanic male specimens collected by Harwood at Colchester in 1900 and 1903. There are also melanic males from Sudbury (1922 and 1923), a dark female (1924) and a paler female (1916) from Sudbury, all from the Harwood's collection. Ashwell collected it at Bishop's Stortford on various dates in 1941, and again in 1944 (Natural History Museum collection). In Suffolk, Sladen (1912) reports a nest of this species discovered in a mole's nest at Bury St. Edmunds in 1898, and Morley (1899) reports it (as var. *subterraneus* of *B. hortorum*) from Tostock, and also (var. *harrisellus*) from Lowestoft. Alford (1975) figures specimens from Essex, and data held by the IBRA relating to the 1980 *Atlas* include records for this species attributed to Alford from Tolleshunt D'Arcy (no date) and Tollesbury (1970). Other records include Finchingfield, 16/8/74 (P.H. Williams), Ongar, 1973 (W. Booker) and Takeley, 1970 (Testro).

During the period of this survey I have one report of a head and genital capsule of what may be from a male of this species, preserved from a squashed specimen found in Braintree, 1988 (S. Burden pers. comm.). S.L. Pennington observed a male foraging from sulphur clover at Dunmow railway cutting on 22/6/91 (identification subsequently confirmed, T. Benton). Another, this time a queen, was found dead by the roadside near Great Chesterford (close to the border with Cambridgeshire) on 12/5/93. Despite repeated searches in subsequent years, no further sightings of the species were made at the Dunmow site. Finally, another queen was observed foraging from cultivated flowers in pots outside a village pub close to Colchester on 28/8/99. This specimen was of a darkened (but not completely black) form, lacking the yellow abdominal band (specimen confirmed as *B. ruderatus* by P.H. Williams and G.R. Else).

Clearly this species has become very scarce, and may be on the verge of extinction in the county. This seems to be the case nationally, given the paucity of records even in its former stronghold at Dungeness. Falk (1991) reiterates the common view that large tracts of suitable habitat are required to sustain the scarcer species of *Bombus*, and that intensification of land-use is a cause of decline. His view is that this species seems to be especially vulnerable to habitat fragmentation. Threats to it include scrubbing over of previously flower-rich grassland, intensive forestry, development, and agricultural improvement, with loss of hedgebanks. This view is reiterated in the National Biodiversity Plan now prepared for this species.

The status of *B. ruderatus* is very puzzling. Since it is reputed to have very populous colonies, it might be expected that it would be observed relatively frequently, even if colonies are few in number. The extreme dispersion of records across the county, and through time seem hard to reconcile with viable breeding populations. Further, there is no obvious ecological similarity among the few sites where it has been observed. One site is urban, one in a flower-rich oasis within largely agricultural countryside, another amid an intensively farmed landscape and, the most recent, cultivated flowers in a small village in similarly intensively farmed countryside. One intriguing possibility is that there are remaining populations that survive in suburban gardens. These are for obvious reasons quite difficult for amateur hymenopterists to access, especially as capture and close examination of specimens is required for reliable determination.

Falk (1991) makes management recommendations for the conservation of this species. These include maintenance of large tracts of unimproved, flower-rich grassland, avoidance of chemical fertilisers and pesticides, and leaving banks, ditches and hedgerows as nesting and hibernation sites. Flowers with long corolla tubes, particularly Fabaceae and Lamiaceae should be encouraged, and ecological succession to scrub opposed, preferably by rotational management. These recommendations would seem to be appropriate for a wide range of *Bombus* species, presumably including *B. ruderatus*, but in the absence of more detailed research into the current status of this species, the reasons for its very rapid decline, and its exact ecological requirements they must remain to a degree speculative. There are no sites in the UK currently known to harbour flourishing populations of this species. Salisbury Plain, in Wiltshire, is one locality matching Falk's recommendations in which the species may still survive. Its previous stronghold at Dungeness is a unique site in Britain (Williams, 1989a). Extensive meadows and arable farmland previously adjacent to this site are now believed to have been important, too, for the exceptional assemblage of bumblebees, including *B. ruderatus*, recorded from this site, and current management initiatives are aimed at restoring this feature (Edwards, 1999). Recent records in Essex do not seem to fit any pattern at all, but it seems that *B. ruderatus* survives here, presumably at very low population levels, in the absence of large tracts of flower-rich habitat (unless suburban gardens count as just that!). Clearly, as indicated in the Biodiversity Action Plan (1999), research into all aspects of the autecology of this endangered bee is urgently required, together with action to protect, and where possible restore, the large areas of suitable habitat which it appears to require.

Bombus pascuorum (Scopoli)

Common carder bee

A very common and wide-
spread species.

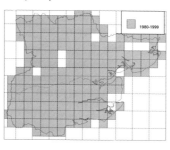

Description

Queens are rather small and
variable in colour pattern, with
relatively long and uneven
coats. There are usually tufts
of yellow-brown hair on the head and face. The thorax is uniformly coloured, lacking
the contrasting bands of many other species, though there are often black hairs mixed
in, especially around the front margin or (in some individuals) forming a triangular
dark patch. The dominant colour varies from yellow-orange to rust-brown. In paler
specimens, the yellow-orange hairs also predominate on the abdomen, though usually
mixed in with varying amounts of black hair which, however, do not form obvious

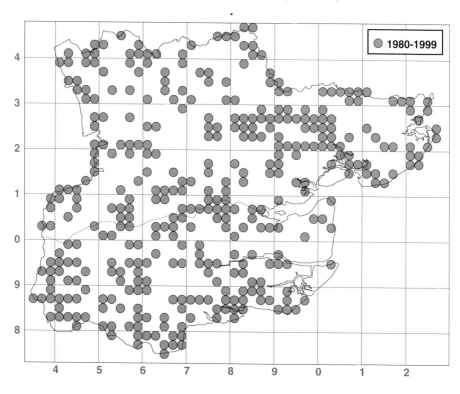

bands. In one common pale form, the pale hairs predominate on each segment of the abdomen, but there are tufts of black hairs at the sides of segments two to five. In somewhat darker forms, these tufts extend across the abdomen, giving the impression of narrow dark bands. In another form, most of the hairs on segment three of the abdomen are black, with just a narrow fringe of yellow hairs along the hind margin. In the darkest forms I have encountered, the thorax is brown, with yellow hairs on segment one of the abdomen, segments two and three almost completely black, and a rust-brown tail. There are several named geographical subspecies in the British Isles, but the degree of individual variation in the Essex populations appears to be as wide as that ascribed to these geographical forms.

Workers are very variable in size, some being very tiny indeed, others overlapping small queens. They are similar in colour-pattern, and exhibit a similar range of variation. In some, the dominant colour is a pale lemon yellow, whilst in others the black hairs on the abdomen are very few, and dispersed among the yellow-orange ones, so that careful examination is needed to separate them from *B. humilis* workers.

Males are also similar in pattern and degree of variation. However, the black hairs on the abdomen tend to be concentrated in narrow bands across the segments (commonly segments two, three and four), rather than tufted at the sides. Pale forms of the male are quite common in Essex. These have very few black hairs on the abdomen, making field discrimination between them and males of *B. humilis* and *B. muscorum* quite difficult where these species fly together.

Identification

The orange-brown, non-banded thorax immediately distinguishes all castes of this species from all but two other species that may be found in Essex. Since the other two are very localised, this feature is enough to provisionally identify *B. pascuorum* over most of the county. Darker specimens, with prominent tufts or bands of black hair on the abdomen, can be reliably identified as *B. pascuorum*. However, confusion with *B. humilis* and *B. muscorum* is possible in the case of those specimens of *B. pascuorum* which lack obvious areas of black hair on the abdomen. The technique (see chapter 1) of tubing and examining live bees in the field can be used in such cases. If, after careful examination (in good light, and viewed from several different angles), no black hairs can be seen on the abdomen, then the specimen is likely to be either *B. muscorum* or *B. humilis* (for distinction between these see under *B. humilis*). An additional feature that can be observed (though with some difficulty – a lateral view is essential.) in males is the different shape of the segments of the antennae (see fig. 5.26). For fully reliable identification, however, microscopic examination of structural characters may be needed. For this purpose, the male genitalia are distinctive (see fig. 5.32 1 m & n) with the added benefit that the taking of a male voucher specimen has little or no significance from the point of view of the conservation of the species.

Life-history

Queens are not generally among the earliest bumblebees to emerge from hibernation, usually appearing a little later than *B. lucorum*, *B. terrestris* and *B. pratorum*, during March, or at the beginning of April (earliest noted, Colchester, 14/3/99). In April, queens alternate between foraging and prospecting for nest-sites. One observed during late afternoon at the Moors, Colchester on 8/4/99 appeared to be prospecting for a nest-site among rank grasses. It eventually disappeared for some minutes (at around 5.15 pm). When I moved the grass stems I found it nestled into mosses below them. There was no sign of a nest, and the obvious inference is that some females of *B. pascuorum* use such situations for roosting between emerging for hibernation and establishing their nests. The individual in question demonstrated its displeasure at the disturbance, by curving its abdomen towards me as if preparing to sting, and buzzing loudly before flying off!

Nests are said to be constructed at or only slightly below ground level. *B. pascuorum*, in common with the other carder bees, constructs a nest out of mosses or other vegetation, woven together among tussocks of grass. The survey organised by Fussell & Corbet (1992a) confirmed the preference of this species for unmown and tussocky grassland, often near hedges or shrubs for its nest-sites. Shuckard (1866) describes the co-operation of workers in extending the nest, biting off filaments of moss, forming them into pellets, and passing them back along chains of workers to the nest. Studies by Brian (1951) showed that egg-batches were laid on cocoons of developing workers in appropriate proportions, so that there were sufficient workers from earlier broods to nourish their successors. She also noted very high rates of mortality (30-40%), especially at late larval and early pupal stages. In this species, the peak number of workers per nest is reputed to be between one hundred and two hundred. In one study (Free & Butler, 1959), more than a half of colonies of this species failed to reach maturity. In those that did males were produced first, then a mixture of males and young queens, and finally queens only. *B. pascuorum* is a pocket-maker, in which there is competition among larvae for food. This is held to explain the divergence in size among workers. According to Free & Butler (1959) the transition to production of males and queens is a result of a change in feeding regime to one in which the workers supplement the diet of the larvae with regurgitated pollen and nectar.

In Essex, the first workers appear at the end of April, or beginning of May, and are observed foraging actively right through the spring and summer into late September or early October (*e.g.* one worker seen with pollen loads on white deadnettle, 30/9/99 at Colchester). In view of the overlap in size between large workers and small queens, it is difficult to be certain from field observations when the first young queens emerge. In some years males are observed as early as the third week in June, and they continue to be observed into late October or early November. Young queens, also, continue to forage at least until late October. D.G. Down observed individuals (caste uncertain) of this species sunning themselves on garden fences in late October and early November 1999 in south-east Essex. Occasionally others would pounce on the resting ones, but no actual copulation was observed, and he concluded all were males (D.G. Down, pers. comm.). There are few, if any, published descriptions of male 'patrolling' behaviour in this species (Fussell & Corbet, 1992c).

Prŷs-Jones & Corbet (1991) state that this species has a long life-cycle and that there is no evidence of a second brood. However, sexual adults are observed from June through to early November, with active workers observed until at least early October. Males observed on 3/10/99 at Hilly Fields, Colchester, appeared to be freshly emerged, and individual males continued to be seen until the end of October. These observations of males and young queens over a period of some four months are consistent with double broods, and are rather difficult to explain in any other way. It could be that some overwintering queens establish colonies very late, or that there are very large differences in the length of time it takes individual colonies to reach maturity. For whatever reason, colonies of this species are by a considerable margin the last to break up in the autumn (except in the extreme south of the county).

Habitat and forage-sources

After hibernation queens forage from a very wide range of flowers, including sallow, blackthorn, creeping buttercup, dove's-foot crane's-bill, red campion, green alkanet, dandelion, bluebell and flowering currant. However, as long-tongued species, they are particularly attracted to flowers with long corolla tubes, and most especially the Lamiaceae. By far their most visited flower in Essex is white deadnettle but they also forage from red deadnettle, ground ivy, bugle and yellow archangel. Later in the year they are also frequent visitors to the flowers of black horehound. According to flowering season they also visit a range of other flowers with long corolla-tubes, such as bluebell, comfrey and various Fabaceae, including fodder, bush and common vetches, red clover, restharrows and narrow-leaved bird's-foot trefoil. Though in Essex less often seen in gardens than other common species, they do frequent the flowers of *Aubrieta*, *Digitalis*, *Lavandula*, *Syringa* and others.

Early in the year the workers are confined to a limited range of forage-sources. As with the queens, the most frequently visited is white deadnettle, with other Lamiaceae (bugle, ground ivy, hedge and marsh woundwort, black horehound), Fabaceae (bird's-foot trefoil, narrow-leaved bird's-foot trefoil, tufted, fodder and bush vetches, meadow vetchling, white and red clover), Asteraceae (marsh, creeping and spear thistles and knapweed), field scabious, red bartsia, comfrey, purple loosestrife, bramble, mallow, and many other species also commonly visited. During the survey, white deadnettle, black horehound, mallow, narrow-leaved bird's-foot trefoil and red bartsia were noted as pollen-sources. Late in the season, red bartsia, black horehound and white deadnettle appear to be particularly important forage-plants for the

Queen	M	A	M	J	J	A	S	O
Sallow (m & f)	V							
Green alkanet	V	V	V					
Comfrey	V							
White deadnettle	V	V	V	V	V			V
Red deadnettle	V	V	V					
Ground ivy	V	V	V					
Creeping buttercup		V						
Dove's foot cranes-bill		V						
Blackthorn		V						
Gorse		V						
Yellow archangel		V						
Dandelion		V						
Bluebell		V	V					
Aubrieta (g)		V						
Flowering currant (g)		V						
Red campion			V					
Bramble			V	V				
Common vetch			V	V				
Comfrey			V	V				
Bugle			V					
Ragwort			V					
Lilac (g)			V					
Miscel. (g)			V	V				
Field bean (a)			V					
Oil-seed rape (a)			V					
Mallow				V				
Fodder vetch				V				
Bush vetch				V				
Hounds tongue				V				
Red clover				V				
Black horehound				V				
Thistles (spp)				V				
Fox-glove (g)				V				
Lavender (g)				V				
Restharrow					V			
Hedge woundwort					V			
Spiny rest-harrow						V		
Purple loosestrife						V		
Narrow-leaved bird's-foot trefoil							V	

Worker	M	A	M	J	J	A	S	O
Sallow (f)	V							
Rosemary (g)	V							
Green alkanet		V	V	V				
White deadnettle		V	V		V	V	P	V
Bramble			V	V	V			
Bird's-foot trefoil			V			P		
Tufted vetch			V					
Red clover			V	V	V		V	
Comfrey			V	V			V	
Bugle			V					
Ground ivy			V					
Rhododendron (g)			V					
Misc. (g)			V	V				
Ragged robin				V				
Creeping cinquefoil				V				
Narrow-leaved bird's-foot trefoil				V	V	V	V	
Fodder vetch				V				
Bush vetch				V				
Meadow vetchling				V	V			
Hound's tongue				V				
White clover				V	V		V	
Hedge woundwort				V	V			
Black horehourid				V	V	V	P	
Wood sage				V	V			
Seff heal				V				
Field scabious				V				
Marsh thistle				V	V			
Creeping thistle				V				
Dandelion				V				
Bellflower (g)				V				
Lavatera (g)				V				
Snowberry(g)				V				
Wild rose					V			
Water figwort					V			
Lesser burdock					V			
Knapweed					V	V		
Lavender (g)					V			
Purple toadflax (g)					V			
Mallow						P		
Marsh woundwort						V		
Common calamint						V		
Water mint						V		
Red bartsia						P		
Spear thistle						V	V	
Himalayan balsam							V	
Purple loosestrife							V	
Welted thistle							V	
Jasmine (g)							V	
Misc. shrubs and herbs (g)							V	

workers. Garden flowers and shrubs visited most frequently include *Aubrieta*, *Symphoricarpos*, *Lavandula*, *Campanula*, *Jasminum* and *Linaria*.

Male	M	A	M	J	J	A	S	O
Spear thistle				V				
Bramble					V		V	
Water mint					V			
Field scabious					V			
Devils-bit scabious					V	V	V	
Creeping thistle					V	V		
Buddleia (g)					V			
Greater bindweed						V		
Common toadflax						V		
Tamarisk								V
Black horehound								P
White deadnettle								V
Ragwort								V

Caste unspecified	M	A	M	J	J	A	S	O
Bird's-foot trefoil		V	V					
Mallow			V					
Foxglove			V					
Lavender (g)			V					
Tufted vetch				V				
Greater bindweed				V				
Privet				V				
Creeping thistle				V		V		
Spiny restharrow					V			
Black horehound					V			V
Rosebay willowherb						V		
Knapweed						V		
Bramble								V
Hebe (g)								V

Males forage from bramble, water mint, greater bindweed, common toadflax and black horehound, as well as a range of summer and autumn-flowering Asteraceae, field scabious and devil's-bit scabious. Males are, of course, foraging to meet their own nutritional requirements only, but do consume pollen as well as nectar (*e.g.* one observed on 30/10/99 at the Moors, Colchester, visiting black horehound, and stopping occasionally to brush pollen on its coat forward with its front legs). As with the queens at this time of year, pollen is of course not collected but consumed directly.

The importance of perennial wild flowers with long corolla tubes such as white deadnettle, black horehound and red bartsia, especially as forage-sources late in the year, is probably why this species is found commonly in urban waste ground, such as public open spaces, disused allotments, roadside verges, hedges and ditches, the edges of footpaths and bridleways, woodland rides and so on. Intensively cultivated land, mown or close-grazed grassland are unsuitable for *B. pascuorum*, and it seems to make less use of private gardens than other common species. Fussell & Corbet (1991) concluded that this species and *B. hortorum* made pollinating visits to agricultural crops such as field bean and red clover but that they require a succession of other forage-sources throughout the season, and uncultivated areas for nesting and hibernating. Though agricultural importance was not of particular concern in the Essex survey, field bean was noted as a forage source for queens of this species.

Distribution and status in Essex

B. pascuorum is a 'Mainland Ubiquitous' species which remains common, often abundant throughout the British Isles. In Essex it remains very common and widespread across the county, having been recorded during this survey in 369 tetrads and in all 57 ten-kilometre squares.

The continued abundance of *B. pascuorum* is in some ways puzzling. It seems likely that it has much in common behaviourally and ecologically with its close relatives which have all undergone rapid declines in recent decades. Three of these (*B. humilis*, *B. sylvarum* and *B. ruderarius*) are mainly southern or south-eastern in their distribution, and so close to the limits of their geographical range. For such species, survival depends on habitats offering higher levels of resources than is the case for species in the middle of their geographical range. Loss, fragmentation and deterioration of habitats would therefore be more likely to adversely affect these species than ones, such as *B. pascuorum*, which are not near their latitudinal limit (see Williams, 1988). Even so, the success of *B. pascuorum* in maintaining apparently viable populations in the context of agricultural intensification and high development pressures deserves further study, which could have considerable value in informing conservation strategies for its threatened relatives.

Bombus humilis Illiger

Though a nationally scarce species, it remains relatively frequent in suitable habitat (where this has so far survived intense development pressure) along the Thames estuary, in the extreme south of the county. The national distribution map is a guide to past range for this species but is very misleading as to its current status.

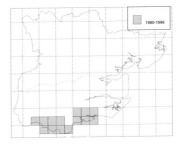

Description

Queens are very similar in appearance to pale queens of *B. pascuorum*. The thorax is yellow-orange and unbanded, but with variable numbers (usually few) of black hairs mixed in. In many specimens these black hairs are very few in number, and clustered round the wing-bases. The dominant coloration of the abdominal hairs is also yellow-

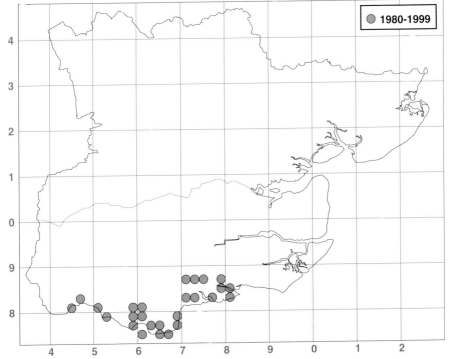

orange, but there is usually a rather indistinct band of darker brownish coloration across the front half of segment two. Sometimes there are similarly coloured, but narrower bands on segments three and four. There are tufts of yellow hair on the head and face. There are no black hairs on the abdomen.

Workers are similar to the queens, but generally considerably smaller. The Essex specimens I have seen vary in ground-colour from yellowish to orange-brown, and have rather more black hairs on the thorax, especially round the wing-bases and at the front of the thorax. Like the queens they have no black hairs on the abdomen. The brownish band on segment two may be indistinct or absent.

Males are very similar to the females, and approximately the same size as the workers. Their longer antennae, longer coat (giving a more furry appearance) and more rounded tip to the abdomen distinguish them from the workers. Essex specimens often lack black hairs on the thorax.

Identification

The coat is said to be shorter and more even than that of *B. pascuorum*, though this is only obvious in the case of the covering of the dorsal surface of the abdomen. Even then, it is only clearly visible when the insect is viewed from the side, and so not very useful as a field-character. Close examination of tubed specimens is needed to establish that there are no black hairs on the abdomen. This character serves to distinguish *B. humilis* from the much more common and widespread *B. pascuorum*. Where close examination is possible, the differently shaped outer segments of the antennae in males provide a good structural character (see fig. 5.26).

However, the third member of this closely related group of carder bees, *B. muscorum,* is very similar to *B. humilis*, and also lacks black hairs on the abdomen. As individuals of *B. muscorum* may also often have a brownish band across segment two of the abdomen, separation of these two species can be difficult. Where there are black hairs on the thorax, this distinguishes *B. humilis* (no black hairs on abdomen or thorax in *B. muscorum*). However, these hairs may be very few in number or even absent (especially in males) in some specimens of *B. humilis* so that this is not a reliable character for distinguishing *humilis* and *muscorum* in Essex. A structural character given in the literature for females is that the hairs at the sides of segment three of the abdomen rise from tiny pits in *B. humilis* and from bumps in *B. muscorum*. However, this character requires microscopic examination, and even then is only really clear in queens. For critical determination, features of the male genitalia appear to be the only reliable characters (see fig. 5.32 l, m & n).

Life-history

Sladen (1912) states that the queens of *B. humilis* emerge from hibernation later than any other species, 'generally not until June'. In Essex, queens are generally observed from mid-May onwards (18/5/98, Fobbing Marshes, P.R.H.; 19/5/99 Wennington Riverside, P.R.H.). However, there is one exceptionally early record (1/4/95, Little Thurrock Marshes, P.R.H.).

Sladen states that this species (as is generally the case with the carder bees) usually nests on the ground. More recent observations by Paul Williams at Dungeness in 1982 (pers. comm.) and by the UK BAP Bumblebee Working Group confirm and add to this. Optimal nesting habitat for this species is a tall but open vegetation structure, allowing the warmth of the sun to penetrate to the base of the grass stems, and with a litter layer of dead grass and/or moss. These latter materials are woven into the nest cover, with evidence that this must be open to the sunlight (Edwards, 1998).

The earliest Essex records for workers are from late May (21/5/95, near Mill Wood Pit, P.R.H.), but they are more commonly found in July, and peak numbers are observed through August. Young queens were observed as early as 26/6/99 (at Benfleet Downs/Hadleigh Castle Country Park, T.B.) and 12/7/92 (at East Tilbury, T.B.), but males are more commonly observed in August (12 and 13/8/94, near Mill Wood Pit and Ferry Fields, Tilbury, respectively, P.R.H.; 12/8/98, Wat Tyler Country Park, T.B.). Late records include foraging workers on 4/9/99 (Canvey Island, T.B.) and a male at Benfleet Downs on 19/9/98. These observations correspond well with those of Paul Williams in Kent, whose males were observed from late July onwards (pers. comm.).

Habitat and forage-sources

As a relatively long-tongued species, *B. humilis* requires areas of flower-rich grassland, with an abundance of flowers with long corolla-tubes, such as the Lamiaceae and Fabaceae. However, the Bumblebee Working Group noted that appropriate nesting sites may be more scarce than foraging habitat. The optimal vegetation structure on Salisbury Plain was provided by long-reverted arable fields, or the edges of tracks where the sward was prevented from becoming too dense, and the litter layer too heavy by disturbance or hay-cutting. Intermittent grazing is beneficial in this respect, but regular or hard grazing prevents the development of a litter layer, essential as a source of nesting materials. *B. humilis*

Queen	M	J	J	A	S
Red clover	V				
Alkanet	V				
Bladder senna			V		
Bird's foot trefoil			V		
Fodder vetch			V		
Common vetch			V		
White clover			V		

Worker	M	J	J	A	S
Red clover			V	P	
Black horsehound			V		
Creeping thistle			V		
Narrow-leaved bird's foot trefoil				P	V
White clover					V

Male	M	J	J	A	S
Black horsehound				V	
Spear thistle				V	V
Knapweed				V	

nests will survive hay-cutting only if the ground is uneven and the cut not thorough. In south Essex the species is found in a surprisingly wide range of habitats, including worked-out and overgrown chalk pits, old, flower-rich grassland, brown-field sites with ruderal vegetation, estuarine grazing marshes and sea walls, and open areas in country parks. Many of these sites are well-drained and nutrient-poor, and are subject to minimal or intermittent management. Perhaps for different reasons, these factors provide environmental conditions comparable with those described for Dungeness by Williams (1998) and at Salisbury Plain by Edwards (1998).

The Bumblebee Working Group give viper's bugloss, kidney vetch, white clover and marsh woundwort as confirmed pollen sources, whilst nectar sources include: sea holly, musk thistle, knapweed, greater knapweed, spear thistle, teasel, field scabious, small scabious, bird's-foot trefoil, lucerne, restharrow, spiny restharrow, red clover, wild basil, mignonette, bramble, dewberry and red bartsia. Williams adds yellow melilot, wood sage, foxglove, toadflax and field pea from his studies in Kent (Williams, 1989a). Pollen analysis from 25 specimens collected in 1998 from a range of U.K. sites revealed a preponderance of clovers and bird's-foot trefoil together with Rosaceae (bramble?), sainfoin and some Asteraceae (thistles) in a smaller number of samples. The loads were generally mixed, but with pollen from a very restricted range (usually only two or three) of flower species in each (Edwards, 1999).

In Essex, queens have been observed foraging in spring on red clover (27/5/99, Benfleet Downs, T.B.) and alkanet (19/5/99, Rainham, P.R.H.). On 7/6/00 they were observed at a bush of bladder senna, on fodder vetch, common vetch and white clover at various sites on Canvey Island (T.B.). Later in the season a young queen was observed foraging from bird's-foot trefoil (26/6/99, Benfleet Downs, T.B.). Through July, August and into September, workers have been observed foraging from red clover, white clover, narrow-leaved bird's-foot trefoil and black horehound. Males visit black horehound, spear thistle and knapweed. No doubt the very limited range of flowers represented in the Essex list could be extended by more systematic observation, but it does suggest that the Essex populations of this species are particularly associated with a small number of flower species in their main foraging habitats. Clovers, bird's-foot trefoils, vetches and black horehound appear to be particularly important in the Essex sites.

Distribution and Conservation

According to Sladen (1912) it was 'not rare' in the Dover district, and it probably occurred throughout the south and east, having been taken 'not uncommonly' in Suffolk, Cambridgeshire, Sussex, Oxfordshire, Hampshire and Devonshire. However, there was considerable confusion between *B. muscorum* and *B. humilis* among earlier entomologists. Specimens collected by Harwood (1898-1903) require further examination. Chapman (1962-66) says that it 'appears now to be one of our less common bees', the only recent record being of a queen at Grays, on 12/8/61. However, the collections in the Natural History Museum (London) contain specimens of all three castes of this species labelled Bishop's Stortford, and collected by D.A. Ashwell in 1940 and 1941. The IBRA/ITE *Atlas* (1980) suggests a very marked decline, with major losses in the north, Midlands and central southern England. There are concentrations of post-1960 records in East Anglia, extreme south-east and south west England and south Wales. Given the (understandable!) confusion with the closely related *B. muscorum*, some of this apparent decline could be the misleading consequence of earlier erroneous records. Nevertheless, the decline was viewed to be sufficiently serious for *B. humilis* to be listed in the U.K. Biodiversity Steering Group Report (1995). A national Biodiversity Action Plan has now been prepared (U.K. Biodiversity Group, 1999).

So far as Essex is concerned, the IBRA/ITE *Atlas* gives four post-1960 ten-kilometre squares. Three of these are in the north east of the county, and a fourth in the south east, in the region of the Crouch estuary. Chapman's (1962-66) record from Grays (a more indicative one, from the standpoint of current knowledge about the species in Essex) seems to have been overlooked. Data held by the IBRA include one record from Alford, at Tolleshunt D'Arcy, another from Fingringhoe Wick in 1972 (W. Hooper) and another from Brentwood (no date). No further details of the dates and localities for the *Atlas* are currently available, but intensive searches of potential habitat in the north east of the county have so far proved fruitless (though, interestingly, *B. muscorum* does occur here).

Post-1980 records in Essex are concentrated in 26 tetrads in 7 ten-kilometre squares along the Thames estuary, in the extreme south of the county. The species is found in suitable patches of habitat from Beckton, east London, in the west, to Benfleet/ Hadleigh Downs and Canvey Island, in the east. So far, the most northerly records are from the Vange and Pitsea areas.

B. humilis thus forms part of the extraordinarily rich aculeate assemblage of the East Thames Corridor which P.R. Harvey, in particular, aas studied intensively. Harvey has been especially active in drawing urgent attention to the degree of threat posed to these habitats by Thames Gateway development proposals, and by already extant development projects and planning permissions. Unique post-industrial sites, pulverised fly ash and silt lagoons, chalk, brick and sand pits as well as remnants of old flower-rich grasslands provide what can now be seen as an unparalleled mosaic of aculeate habitats, but on current planning presumptions such 'brown field' sites are especially vulnerable to development. As Harvey points out (*e.g.* in relation to Mill Wood Pit) mitigation in relation to such development proposals simply does not take into account the importance of extensive mosaics of habitat:

'The Penny Anderson Associates report recognises the importance of the Mill Wood Pit site *'the high diversity reflects the range of habitats present and in particular the extensive nature of the chalk and sand grassland, sand cliffs and scattered scrub communities in the southwest zone of Chafford Hundred'*, but on the other hand claims that the destruction of almost all this habitat will still result in the conservation of at least 73% of the RDB and Notable species!' (Harvey, 1997).

Although some sites (notably Wat Tyler Country Park, and the Benfleet Downs/Hadleigh Castle complex) which currently hold substantial populations of *B. humilis* can be regarded as 'safe' from such pressures, it is unlikely that viable populations of this species could be wholly sustained on these sites in the context of development of adjacent tracts of land despite the fact that this species appears to have higher nesting densities than other southern species (Edwards, 1998). Sustained and effective intervention on behalf of this and other threatened species in the remaining Thames Corridor sites on the part of local authorities and statutory bodies is urgently required.

This needs to be (and, at the time of writing, is being) supplemented by management regimes designed to increase the carrying capacity of secure sites for populations of *B. humilis* and other scarce and threatened species. More research is needed to determine the exact habitat requirements of this species in Essex, but it seems that the tall but open and flower-rich grasslands which are characteristic of the meadows on the south-facing scarp of Benfleet/Hadleigh Downs, together with the wide ride-margins through scrub and secondary woodland which connect them currently provide good habitat. Cautious and carefully monitored extension of this regime to areas currently scrubbed over is likely to be beneficial. Late (end of September or later) or rotational grass-cutting is desirable. Cutting in August or earlier is liable to be disastrous for a species which nests on the ground and whose colonies appear often not to reach maturity until August or later. As suggested in the national BAP for this species (UK Biodiversity Group, 1999), agri-environmental schemes could well be directed to extending suitable habitat in agricultural land adjacent to its currently known habitats. However, the most immediate threats to its remaining Essex populations are development pressures along the Thames estuary (see Harvey in Edwards, 1999).

Bombus muscorum (Linnaeus)

This has always been a scarce and localised species in Essex, and currently seems to be declining rapidly.

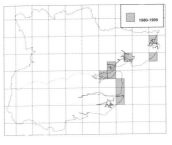

Description

Queens are said to be slightly larger than those of *B. pascuorum* and *B. humilis* (Sladen, 1912). However, in general appearance they are very similar. The ground-colour of the coat covering the thorax and abdomen is orange-brown, sometimes with a darker brown, but indistinct band on segment two of the abdomen. There are no black hairs mixed in with the orange-brown, either on the thorax or the abdomen.

Workers are very similar to the queens, but smaller. The coat is slightly longer than that of *B. humilis*, and very even, giving a distinctive 'crew-cut' appearance.

Males are similar in appearance, and roughly of the same size as the workers.

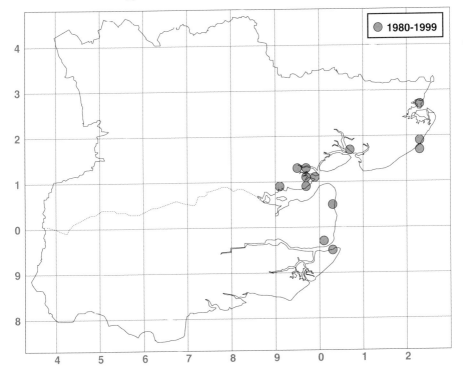

Identification

See under *B. pascuorum* and *B. humilis*. For provisional identification in the field, the lack of black hairs on either thorax or abdomen, together with the even, 'crew-cut' appearance are helpful. Queens can be distinguished from those of *B. humilis* by microscopic examination of the surface of the side of the third abdominal segment (see under *B. humilis*). The male genitalia are distinctive (fig. 5.32 l, m & n).

Life-history

As is the case with other scarce or local species, the queens emerge from hibernation relatively late in the spring. Laidlaw (1931), reported large numbers of over-wintered queens on red deadnettle. There are very few observations of over-wintering queens in Essex. Two seen on 19/6/00 on Old Hall Marsh were foraging from white clover and common vetch, and another was seen on 6/6/93 at Holland Haven (T.B.). Like other carder bees, *B. muscorum* builds nests on or near the surface of the ground, using dead grasses or moss as materials. The nesting habitat is the same as for *B. humilis,* but generally in damper localities (M. Edwards, pers. comm.). The earliest date noted for workers in Essex is late May (23/5/98, Old Hall Marsh nature reserve, T.B.), and their numbers build to a peak in late June or July. Even at their peak, however, numbers of individual workers are always very small (maximum observed at one site was approximately fifteen on 29/6/92 at Holland Haven, near Frinton, T.B.). Workers of this species seem to be unusually irritable, and easily disturbed by approaching humans, making photography quite difficult, for example. They are also reputedly quite fierce in the defence of their nests. An entertaining passage from Sladen's classic work is worth quoting at length:

> *'In July 1911, having been informed by some labourers in these marshes who were mowing the hay there, that they frequently came across the nests of a savage yellow bee which they feared to disturb more than a wasps' nest, I asked them when they next found a nest to let me know, and on July 21 was summoned to take two nests, both of this species, situated only about ten yards apart in a hay field. So great was the men's fear of getting stung that they did not dare to approach near enough to show me the exact spots, and I found that, as soon as I disturbed the nests, the workers flew round my head in a most menacing manner; they also had the disagreeable trick of persisting in doing this, following me wherever I went for a minute or two.'* (Sladen, 1912)

The earliest male so far recorded in the Essex populations was the end of June (29/6/92, Holland Haven, T.B.). Males continue to be seen until late August (*e.g.* 22/8/98, Old Hall, T.B.), and colonies break up by the end of August (e.g, a few workers, probably foraging for their own nutrition, on 27/8/93, Holland Haven, T.B.).

Williams reports that in Kent queens emerge from hibernation in early June, with the first appearance of workers following in mid- to late June, and males in July (Williams, 1989a). This is consistent with the rather sparse Essex observations.

Habitat and forage-sources

Sladen notes that the species in Kent is confined to marshy districts, and is commonest in cold, damp seasons (Sladen, 1912). He gives marsh mallow and clover as forage-sources. Alford (1975) lists several Lamiaceae, thistles and Ericaceae. Williams (1988) gives marshy, open areas without drastic frequent disturbance as its habitat in Kent. In Essex, the species now appears to be confined to coastal marshes and sea walls, where its forage-sources are more limited in variety. Several species of Fabaceae appear to be particularly important in these localities.

Workers have been observed to visit bird's-foot trefoils, tufted vetch, meadow vetchling, spiny restharrow and white, red, zig-zag and sea clover. Most sites contain an abundance of clover and bird's-foot trefoil flowers. Slender and creeping thistle are also visited (the former for pollen, along with red clover), and other Asteraceae, especially late in the season. Males have been observed on narrow-leaved bird's-foot trefoil and spear thistle. Williams (1989a) adds viper's bugloss, teasel and field pea as forage plants in Kent.

Distribution and Conservation

Sladen (1912) states that this species is not abundant, but is widespread thoughout Britain, being more common in Scotland and Ireland than in England. It occurs, on off-shore islands, with distinct named forms. According to the IBRA/ITE *Atlas* (1980), there is some evidence of decline in the post-1960 data. However, the species has never been recorded at more than a few sites in central-southern and the midlands of England. Its rather sparse post-1960 distribution in England and Wales is primarily coastal. Kent remained its southern stronghold during that period, with records along the north and east coasts of the county, and concentrations in marshy areas near Dungeness and Eastbourne in the south (Williams, 1989a).

In Essex, Harwood (1884) reported unwittingly disturbing a nest of '*Bombus cognatus* Steph.' on St Osyth coast, 'the proprietors of which came buzzing about my head in a very menacing manner'. He considered it a common

Queen	M	J	J	A
White clover		V		
Common vetch		V		

Worker	M	J	J	A
Slender thistle	P			
Narrow-leaved bird's foot trefoil		V	V	
Bird's-foot trefoil		V		
Tufted vetch		V	P	
Meadow vetching		V		
White clover		P	V	
Red clover		P	P	
Sea clover		V		
Creeping thistle		V		V
Spiny restharrow			V	
Zigzag clover			V	
Cat's-ears				V
Sea aster				V

Male	M	J	J	A
Narrow-leaved bird's foot trefoil		V		
Spear thistle				V

species, especially towards the coast. In the same journal, Saunders (1884), who Harwood thanks for help with identifications, gives descriptions which point to '*B. cognatus*' being a synonym for what we now know as *B. muscorum*. Then, as now, the species was mainly coastal, and there is an interesting parallel between Harwood's story and Sladen's account of 'menacing' behaviour! Harwood collected it in the Colchester district in 1899, and 1906 (IBRA data) and Chapman (1962-66) reports three subsequent records: Skipper's Island, 16/4/60, and Thorpe-le-Soken,12/6/60, both by R.J. Knowles, and Layer-de-la-Haye, 24/9/61, presumably by Chapman himself. Chapman comments that it is 'one of our less common species', and supposes it to be confined, in the southern and eastern counties of England, chiefly to marshy districts. The IBRA/ITE *Atlas* gives only two Essex ten-kilometre squares, both on the east coast. IBRA data include one record from Alford, at Tolleshunt D'Arcy. During the current survey it has proved possible to locate only small and scattered populations along the east coast, confined to remnants of coastal grazing marsh and the strips of rough grassland between sea walls and borrow-dykes. These sites are spread out between Little Oakley in the north and Foulness in the south, and are included in a mere thirteen tetrads in seven ten-kilometre squares. It seems very unlikely that the species has expanded its range in the county since the data for the IBRA/ITE *Atlas* were collected, and the greater number of post-1980 records probably reflects more thorough fieldwork. Workers of this species commonly forage in company with workers of *B. lapidarius*, and on some sites with *B. ruderarius*. They are always, however, massively outnumbered by other species, particularly by *B. lapidarius*.

Repeated visits to Old Hall Marshes, Brightlingsea Marsh and Tollesbury Wick Marsh in recent years confirm that the species holds on there in very small numbers. The Essex 'stronghold' for this species was the area of grazing marsh, now Holland Haven Country Park, between Frinton and Holland-on-Sea, and along the adjacent Frinton Golf Course. Repeated searches in 1997, 98 and 99 proved fruitless, and it began to appear that the species had become extinct at this site. However, visits on 17th and 18th July 2000 confirmed the continued presence of *B. muscorum*, up to eight workers being seen on each occasion, mainly foraging on dense patches of tufted vetch. More than 15 individuals, a mixture of males and workers, were observed at Old Hall Marsh on 18th August 2000. The apparent recovery of this species at these times is in agreement with Sladen's (1912) observation that *B. muscorum* flourishes best in damp seasons. Other records are of (usually singleton) workers foraging on Fabaceae on rough grassland between sea walls and borrow-dykes where former inland grazing marshes have been converted to arable. It has not proved possible to re-visit these locations, and it remains unclear whether populations can survive on such remaining strips of habitat. On balance it seems likely that extensive areas of grazing marsh are required, but clearly more research is needed.

A rather striking feature of the distribution of this species is its confinement to the estuarine and coastal marshes of east Essex, whilst its close relative, *B. humilis* (elsewhere sometimes found flying together with *B. muscorum, e.g.* at Dungeness (Williams, 1989a)) appears to have an entirely disjunct range along the southern fringe of the county. Interestingly, the south side of the Thames estuary, in north Kent, appears to be mainly (but not exclusively, see Williams, 1985) occupied by *B. muscorum*. Williams (in Edwards, 1998) has suggested that this interesting pattern may have to do with the different aspects of the two coasts of the Thames estuary – the northern one southerly and warmer, the southern one northerly in aspect and cooler. Clearly micro-climate as well as availability of suitable nesting and foraging habitat is a significant factor in the distribution of both species in Essex.

Although *B. muscorum* is regarded as a 'Widespread Local' species in the UK as a whole, and was not included for special attention in the UK Biodiversity Action Plan, its status in Essex seems very precarious indeed. This also appears now to be the situation nationally (M. Edwards, pers. comm.). Its existence on Foulness has only just been established (P.R. Harvey, pers. comm.) and it may occur on MoD land not so far surveyed, but there are known viable populations on only three remaining extensive tracts of grazing marsh. Local action is required to ascertain its current status in the county, and to research its ecological requirements so that appropriate management regimes can be put in place wherever this is practicable. In the absence of a national BAP, a local Action Plan at county level would clearly be appropriate. Agri-environmental schemes targeted at benefiting this species on former grazing marshes, or adjacent farmland, should be considered.

Bombus ruderarius (Müller)

Red-shanked bumblebee

A nationally declining species, which remains widespread, if rather local, in Essex.

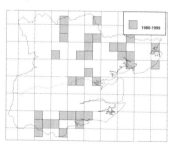

Description

Queens are rather small, and the coat is black except for a red tail. The corbicular hairs (on the hind tibia) are mainly orange-red (but may be black at the base).

Workers are similarly coloured, but smaller. The corbicular hairs may be darker, and orange-red only towards the outer tip.

Males are quite variable in colour pattern. Dark forms look quite similar to the workers, with indistinct clusters of yellow-brown hairs mixed in with the black on the collar and scutellum, with black abdomen, and red tail. In pale forms, there are wide

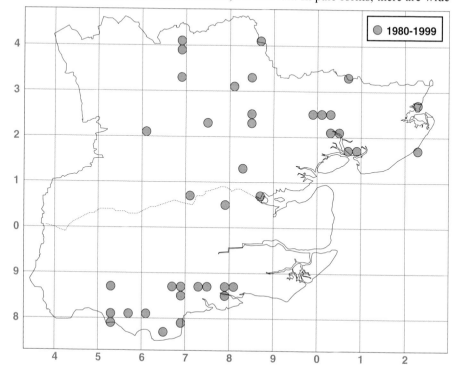

yellowish bands (of more-or-less equal width), on the collar and scutellum, and a wide band of similar colour on segments one and two of the abdomen. Segment three of the abdomen is black, and the tail red. In yet another common form, the tail is a pale, rusty yellow.

Identification

In Essex, queens and workers are likely to be confused only with *B. lapidarius*. In the case of the queens, the smaller size of *B. ruderarius*, and the colour of the corbicular hairs (black in *B. lapidarius*) are distinctive characters. In fresh queens, especially, the black coat of *B. lapidarius* is rich and velvety in appearance, whilst that of *B. ruderarius* is dull and sooty black. Commonly, too, the tail of *B. lapidarius* is a richer red, whilst that of *B. ruderarius* is more rusty, or even yellowish in pale specimens. For critical identification, the structure of the sting sheaths is distinctive, and *B. ruderarius* has a small spine on the apex of the mid-basitarsus, which is lacking in *B. lapidarius* (see fig. 5.31 a & b, and 5.13 a & b). However, this feature of *B. ruderarius* is hard to detect, even with microscopic examination, as it is short, and surrounded with sturdy hairs. The colour of the corbicular hairs is less distinctive in the workers, and confusion can arise from discoloration by pollen, or fading in ageing specimens of *B. lapidarius*.

Males could be confused with males of *B. lapidarius*, *B. sylvarum* or *B. pratorum*. In the case of pale specimens of *B. ruderarius* and *B. lapidarius*, the yellow of the latter is generally brighter, and the yellow on the scutellum is absent, or clearly less than on the collar. Males of *B. pratorum* may also resemble pale specimens of *B. ruderarius*, but they lack yellow hairs on the scutellum. Separation of *B. ruderarius* and *B. sylvarum* males is more difficult, and requires microscopic examination. The relative lengths of the third and fourth antennal segments and details of the male genitalia (see fig. 5.22 a & b, and 5.32 a & k) are distinctive.

Life-history

Females emerge from hibernation a little later than the commoner species, at the beginning of April, or later. However, they establish nests soon afterwards. Queens with pollen loads are observed from the second week in April onwards (*e.g.* 8/4/99, the Moors, Colchester, T.B.). Queens prospect for nest-sites in a manner similar to that noted for *B. terrestris* and *B. lucorum*, among tussocky grasses, and especially in the vicinity of shrubs. While some queens have already established nests during April, others may still be observed prospecting for nest sites into mid-May. According to M. Edwards and E.G. Philp (in Edwards, 1999) the nest is constructed of grass clippings and moss on or just under the ground, among long vegetation. An old mouse nest is often used as a foundation. Sladen (1912) states that the first batch of cocoons in the nest are always, in the examples seen by him, eight in number, and symmetrically arranged. At maturity a nest may have from 50 to 100 workers. The workers are first seen at the end of April and may be observed foraging through the spring and summer until the colonies break up at the end of August or early September (worker noted at Canvey, 4/9/99, T.B.). Males and young queens are produced from the second week in July onwards (*e.g.* males on 10/7/98, Canvey Island, and 14/7/92, Middlewick Ranges, Colchester, T.B.). Both males and queens are more commonly seen through August.

Habitat and forage-sources

Edwards and Philp (in Edwards, 1999) state that this species (like many others) requires extensive areas which support a variety of flowering plants, especially Fabaceae and Lamiaceae. It is essential that suitable forage-plants are available throughout the flight period of the colony. In Essex the species is found on coastal and estuarine grazing marshes, ruderal habitats, especially along the east Thames corridor, country parks, and in a wide variety of other flower-rich sites, often in relatively little-managed public open spaces and waste ground in urban areas. In some of its eastern marshland localities it flies together with *B. muscorum*, and in south Essex is found together with *B. sylvarum* and/or *B. humilis* at several sites.

Queen	A	M	J	J	A
Red clover	V				
Red deadnettle	V		V		
Common vetch	V		V		
White deadnettle	P	V			
Comfrey		V			
White clover			V		
Bird's-foot trefoil					V

Worker	A	M	J	J	A
White deadnettle	V	V	V		
Bird's-foot trefoil		V			
Comfrey		V			
White clover		V	V		
Mallow			V		
Bramble			V		
Narrow-leaved bird's-foot trefoil			V		
Melilot			V		
Dyer's greenweed			V		
Red deadnettle			V		
Red clover				V	
Spear thistle					V

Male	A	M	J	J	A
White clover				V	
Teasel				V	
Knapweed					V

After hibernation, queens alternate between prospecting for nest sites and foraging. At first they meet their own nutritional requirements, and can be observed visiting common vetch, red deadnettle, red clover and white deadnettle. In urban sites they favour white deadnettle, and this appears to be their main pollen source at this time of year. Foraging is very systematic, beginning with the lower whorls of white deadnettle flowers, and progressively moving upwards before moving on to the next plant. They are less easy to approach than other species, and when disturbed fly round the intruder, before flying off at a considerable height. Workers also visit white deadnettle, as well as red deadnettle, mallow, bramble and a range of Fabaceae (including bird's-foot trefoils, dyer's greenweed, melilot and red clover). Males seem particularly attracted to teasels, and have also been recorded at knapweed and white clover. Young queens have been observed at bird's-foot trefoil.

Distribution and Conservation

Sladen (1912) regarded this as a widely distributed species, 'common in many places, especially in the north of England'. A distribution map prepared by Edwards, Philp & Roberts (in Edwards, 1999) shows a predominantly south-eastern distribution, most post-1970 records being concentrated south and east of a line from the Wash to the Bristol Channel, but with a scattering across Wales, the English North and Midlands, Ireland, and a few Scottish outliers. Edwards & Philp comment that the species 'has seen a catastrophic decline in its abundance and distribution throughout the British Isles since the first half of the century', and note that 'the strongest modern populations correspond with the larger areas of unimproved grasslands'.

W.H. Harwood collected it in the Colchester district in 1894, but Chapman (1962-66) reports no subsequent records. However, the IBRA archive of records entered into the 1980 *Atlas* contains numerous records of this species in Essex during the 1960s and early 1970s. Localities include Chigwell, Ongar, Waltham Abbey, Finchingfield, Radwinter, Felsted, Ilford, Saffron Walden, Writtle, Leigh-on-Sea, Ardleigh and Tolleshunt D'Arcy. It is difficult to estimate the extent of recent decline, but in the 1990s it has been found across the county, generally in small and localised populations. In all, it has been recorded during the present survey from 39 tetrads, distributed across 22 ten-kilometre squares. Owing to the similarity between *B. ruderarius* and *B. lapidarius* workers, and the fact that they commonly forage together, it may be that *B. ruderarius* is under-recorded. It has strongholds in remaining coastal and estuarine marshes, in a string of sites along the Thames estuary, and in urban open spaces in the Colchester district, such as the Moors, Bull Meadow, along the River Colne, and Hilly Fields. In such sites the association with white deadnettle is very strong.

It seems likely that where it currently coexists in the east Essex marshes with *B. muscorum*, and in south Essex with *B. humilis* and *B. sylvarum,* conservation measures aimed at these other local or scarce species will benefit *B. ruderarius.* The persistence of localised populations in agricultural mid-Essex suggests that it may benefit from more environmentally benign farming methods, and re-colonise lost territory if sufficient uncultivated marginal land is provided. It nests slightly underground, and has less specialised requirements of vegetation structure than *B. humilis* and *B. muscorum.* This may explain why it has survived longer than these species in intensively farmed areas. However, it is suffering a severe decline nationally (M. Edwards, pers. comm.). The urban populations face two principal threats. One is from development on brown-field sites, so it is important that public authorities are made aware of the conservation and informal amenity value of these sites. The second threat is the tendency to over-manage and formalise what open spaces and waste-ground continue to exist. Again, a different, more 'untidiness-tolerant' aesthetic needs to be encouraged both among the public and land-managers. A slogan proposed by a discussion-group at a recent Essex County Council seminar seems appropriate: 'Keep Essex Untidy'!

Bombus sylvarum (Linnaeus)

Shrill carder bee

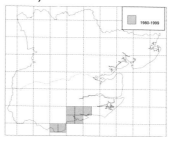 

This is a national priority Biodiversity Action Plan species, with nationally important remaining populations in south Essex. As with other declining species, the national map represents past range only. See text for current distribution.

Description

Queens are small, and relatively inconspicuous. There are pale hairs on the head and face. The thorax has a central band of black hair, with whitish yellow bands on the collar and scutellum. The first segment of the abdomen has pale hairs, the second is predominantly black, as is the third, but with a fringe of pale hairs at the front. The tail is mainly yellow-orange.

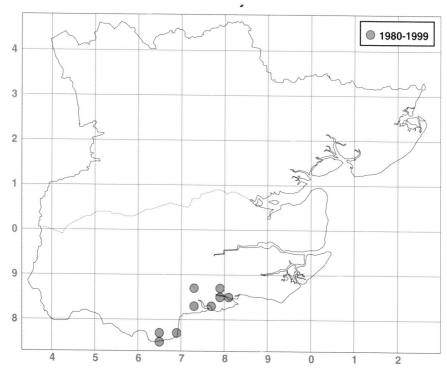

Workers resemble the queens in colouration and patterning, but are very small.

Males are also similarly coloured.

Identification

The workers of this species are very inconspicuous. They lack the bright and contrasting colour patterns of many *Bombus* species, and they tend to be very small. They also have a preference for visiting forage-plants which are over-topped by tall grasses or other vegetation, and so have to be searched for as they weave their way among a jungle of grass stems, thistles, knapweeds and the like. One useful way of locating them is by the sound they make - the shrill, high-pitched buzz referred to in the vernacular name. Where the species forages alongside *B. humilis* workers the difference in pitch between the two species is quite evident. The colour pattern of the females is quite distinctive (although possible confusion with worn and 'balding' *B. pascuorum* workers should be noted), but the males could be confused with pale forms of *B. ruderarius*, which also has two yellowish bands on the thorax and a red/orange tail. In *B. ruderarius* the third segment of the antennae is markedly longer than the fourth, whereas in *B. sylvarum* males, it is only slightly so. There are also small, but fairly clear differences in the male genitalia (a blunt inner projection on the volcella of *B. sylvarum*, but not *B. ruderarius*, see figs 5.22 a & b and 5.32 a & k).

Life-history

According to Sladen (1912), the queens emerge late from hibernation. Over-wintered queens have not often been seen in Essex, but one was observed at Benfleet Downs on 27/5/99, and a dozen or more were seen at various sites on Canvey Island on 7/6/00. The earliest date for workers seen during the current survey is 26/6/99, at Benfleet (one only, T.B.). It seems that colonies build up slowly during July and appear to be at their peak during August - the month in which the overwhelming majority of sightings have been made. Sightings of males range between the second week of August (9/8/98, Wat Tyler Country Park, P.R.H.) and the end of September (28/9/99, Canvey Island, R.G.P.). This pattern is broadly consistent with Williams's observations in Kent: queens emerging from hibernation in late May, workers appearing in early July, and males from late July (Williams, 1989).

The nests are generally on the ground in a slight hollow, or slightly underground though Sladen reports often finding them underground, with a short tunnel. Two nests found by Paul Williams at Dungeness in 1982 were also underground, with tunnels (pers. comm.). Dead litter is required for nesting materials, and it seems that, unlike *B. humilis*, this species does not need its nests to be exposed to the sun. It may, therefore, nest in denser grassland than *B. humilis*, and use old vole runs (Edwards, 1998). Even at their peak, workers number less than one hundred per nest. Philp (in Edwards, 1998) gives late August and September for the emergence of the new generation of males and females, but Essex and Kent dates are somewhat earlier than this.

Habitat and forage-sources

Philp (in Edwards, 1998) gives 'open, flower-rich situations', including sand dunes, edges of salt-marshes, shingle beaches, chalk downland and heathland. Williams reports sandy, open areas without drastic frequent disturbance as habitat in Kent (Williams, 1988). Edwards (1998), reporting on the field research carried out by the Bumblebee Working Group, suggests that the species was possibly associated with hedgerows and headlands in the days of small mixed farms. Current populations seem to occur mainly where similar conditions apply: tall, but open grasslands, herb-rich, and in early stages in the succession of disturbed grassland to scrub. Red bartsia is a typical floral component of such habitats.

The sites so far studied in south Essex include old, flower-rich grassland round the margins of a worked-out mineral extraction site, a former industrial site (now a country park), a south-facing scarp on the Thames estuary, with a mixture of scrub, secondary woodland, and open, flowery grassland (also managed as a country park) and has more recently been discovered by R.G. Payne in another brown-field site on Canvey Island, by P.R. Harvey at East Tilbury silt lagoons and at Hadleigh Castle, Belton Hills and Two Tree Island. All sites are characterised by abundant forage-plants, especially Fabaceae (notably bird's-foot trefoils and clovers), and/or red bartsia. See Williams, 1988 and 1989a).

Queen	M	J	J	A	S
White clover	V				
Red clover	P	V			
Bladder senna		V			
Fodder vetch		V			
Common vetch		V			
Everlasting pea		V			

Worker	M	J	J	A	S
Black horehound		V	P		
Bramble			V		V
Narrow-leaved bird's-foot trefoil			V	P	P
Bird's foot trefoil				P	
White clover				P	V
Red Clover				P	
Wild basil				V	
Red bartsia				P	
Creeping thistle				V	
Bristly oxtongue					V

Male	M	J	J	A	S
Ragwort			V		
Creeping thistle			V		
Knapweed			V		
Spear thistle					V

The queen observed on 27/5/99 at Benfleet Downs was foraging from 4.00 p.m. onwards in a sheltered corner of a south-facing meadow, in an area of greatest density of red clover. It worked each flower-head systematically, dipping its head into each floret in turn as it moved round the flower-head. Before flying on to the next flower-head it stretched its legs out under it and brushed pollen forwards over its thorax and head. There were no pollen loads, and the insect was presumably meeting its own nutritional needs (pollen consumption is important for the maturation of the ovaries in over-wintered queens – Alford 1975 and M. Edwards, pers. comm.). Periodically, it ceased foraging and settled in nearby vegetation, at first combing more pollen forward, and then apparently just sunbathing. Numerous queens observed on Canvey Island on 7/6/00 were visiting the flowers of a solitary bush of bladder senna (up to four individuals at any one time), along with queens of *B. humilis.* They also visited patches of fodder vetch and common vetch close to the sea wall. They also made less frequent visits to red clover, which was also common in the habitat. No pollen collection was observed, and they appeared to be foraging only to meet their own nutritional requirements.

Workers have been observed to visit black horehound, bird's-foot trefoils, red bartsia, wild basil, red and white clovers, creeping thistle and bristly oxtongue. It seems that Fabaceae, especially clovers and bird's-foot trefoils, may be important as both nectar and pollen sources early in the season. Flowering of these plants is extended in some cutting or grazing regimes, and workers are still observed visiting white clover and bird's-foot trefoil into September. Interestingly, on 25/8/98 workers observed at Benfleet Downs were foraging on large patches of narrow-leaved bird's-foot trefoil (some had pollen loads, but none full) in the same meadow where the queen was seen the following spring. They were foraging exclusively on trefoil, even though red bartsia was present. Other observers did see workers visiting red bartsia at this site, and numerous observers have witnessed their evident preference for this plant at Wat Tyler Country Park. At this site, the red bartsia grows among tall grasses, knapweeds, and thistles in the uncut wide margins of tracks through scrub. On 12/8/98 a group of observers counted some twenty individual workers, and a single male. The workers typically visited plants of red bartsia which were almost obscured by surrounding and over-topping rank vegetation, avoiding more exposed patches of the plant. They appeared to be collecting pollen. Occasional short visits were paid to similarly over-topped flowers of bird's-foot trefoil and wild basil. One visit to creeping thistle was noted. Analysis of pollen-loads collected in 1998, in various parts of the UK, confirms the importance of clovers and bird's-foot trefoil in addition to red bartsia as pollen sources. Two Essex samples contained mainly bird's-foot trefoil and clover pollen despite the proximity of flowering red bartsia (Edwards, 1999).

Numbers of foraging workers were particularly concentrated along the wide margins of a sunny junction of tracks. On 19/8/98 it was noted that this particular junction had areas of bartsia exposed to the sun for most of the day, owing to its multiple aspects. Workers were still foraging here when I left at 6.00 p.m. At the Canvey Island site, *B. sylvarum* workers were foraging mainly on extensive areas of narrow-leaved bird's-foot trefoil on 4/9/99. They were collecting pollen from these flowers, stopping occasionally to brush pollen into their corbicula. The shrill buzz is emitted while moving from flower to flower, but the insects are often silent on longer flights. One worn worker was observed foraging on flower-heads of bristly oxtongue (abundant at the site, but ignored by other workers). On closer examination it could be seen that the corbicular hairs were almost worn away on this individual, and it would probably not have been able to carry a pollen-load. There were fewer workers at the site than had been observed earlier on 21 and 23 August by P.R.H. and 29 August by R.G.P. (See Harvey, 2000) suggesting that colonies were in decline by this date.

Summarising current observations on the Essex populations, Harvey (1999b) gives the following provisional conclusions:

1. Red bartsia as a forage source later in the season, when other important sources, such as red clover, are no longer in flower.

2. Tall, flower-rich herbage into late summer.

3. The presence of scrub. This may be correlated with observations of *B. sylvarum* because it is indicative of appropriate management around scrub-edges in such sites. However, scrub edge may also be important as providing protection for nest sites and/or for small mammal habitat.

4. Since this species nests later in the season than most others, reaching maturity during August, abundant forage-sources (especially flowers with long corolla tubes) need to be available at that time of year (Williams 1988, 1989a and 1989b, and Harvey, 1999b). Continuity of forage through the season is important, and forage success during August may be very important.

These are valuable points, and are based on careful observation. However, most of our observations so far have been confined to the foraging behaviour of workers in July and August, and a small number of over-wintered queens. Bumblebee habitat requirements include not just forage-sites, but also appropriate habitat for nesting and hibernation. Rather little is known about these aspects of the behaviour of *B. sylvarum*, and consequently little is known about the 'partial habitats' upon which they depend for these activities. In particular, it is still unknown how far workers travel from nests to forage-sites. So far as foraging-sites, and probably also nesting-sites are concerned, a crucial feature is likely to be that tall vegetation is not cut until autumn or winter, or else cut or grazed intermittently or on rotation. It might also be added that as a southern species, with a very restricted Essex distribution in the extreme south, it seems likely that microclimate, and particularly the aspect of foraging and nesting habitats is important. On-going research funded by English Nature, and conducted by P.R. Harvey, is already revealing new insights into the ecology and conservation of this species in Essex.

Distribution and conservation

Sladen noted that the species was then 'widely distributed in England and Ireland, and common in a good many places' (Sladen, 1912). Morley (1899) gives a number of Suffolk localities: Tostock, Brandon ('common'), and Bramford, near Ipswich ('not infrequent'). Harwood (1884) listed it as 'not common' in the Colchester district and there are specimens collected by him in 1900, 1908 and 1911. The Natural History Museum also has specimens from St Osyth coast (1921) and Sudbury (1919 and 1925). Falk (1991) gives references indicating local abundance in several counties (Glamorganshire, Bedfordshire, Gloucestershire, Cambridgeshire and Devon) during the first half of the 20th century. However, there has subsequently been a very rapid decline. This was noted by Williams in his 1986 publication. The IBRA/ITE *Atlas* showed decline to less than 50% of its previous distribution, with only approximately 80 post-1960 ten-kilometre-square records. On this basis it was classed as a 'notable B' species (Falk, 1991). However, a later map, compiled by Edwards & Roberts (in Edwards, 1998) gave only 51 post-1970 confirmed ten-kilometre square records in England and Wales. On this basis Philp (in Edwards, 1998) concludes that it 'has become much more rare in recent years and may now be in danger of becoming extinct'. The decline of *B. sylvarum* was such that it was short-listed in the UK BAP, and was the first bumblebee species to receive a national Species Action Plan (UK Biodiversity Steering Group, 1995). The newly formed Bumblebee Working Group made a priority of research into this species in 1997. Despite extensive searches of sites where the species had been reported since 1970 (and in some cases earlier), it was found at only three locations: near Sittingourne, in Kent, Salisbury Plain, and Margham Moors, near Swansea (Edwards, 1997). The following year, more individuals were observed, and, by 1999, a total of only six populations had been confirmed in widely dispersed parts of southern England and Wales: the Thames Corridor (north Kent and south Essex localities), Salisbury Plain, Somerset Levels, Newport Levels, Kenfig/Margam Moors, S. Wales and Castlemartin Ranges, S. Wales.

In Essex, Chapman (1962) gives Navestock Park, 20/8/1960 as the only Essex record since Harwood. The data held be the IBRA add: Fingringhoe Wick (1972), Victoria Park (no date), Brentwood (1972), Chigwell and Ongar (both 1973). My own searches from the mid 1980s proved fruitless, and I had come to the view that the species was extinct in Essex, when P.R. Harvey discovered it at Wat Tyler Country Park on 25/8/93. He subsequently observed it on 15/8/94 and later in numbers at Ferry Fields, Tilbury and also at East Tilbury silt lagoons. I found it at Broom Hill, near West Tilbury on 19/8/96. Then, in 1998, P.R. Harvey discovered the species at the Benfleet/Hadleigh Downs complex on 7 August, and on 28/7/99 R.G. Payne discovered workers at a site on Canvey Island. Continuing searches in 2000 have revealed its presence in several more sites, including Belton Hills, Hadleigh Castle and Two Tree Island. Its recent confirmed distribution in Essex thus includes a mere nine tetrads in three ten-kilometre squares, clustered along the Thames estuary, and potentially very vulnerable to development pressures.

R.G. Payne, P.R. Harvey and I have independently surveyed the complex of Essex Wildlife Trust reserve and Country Park south of Laindon and Basildon. Much of this extensive area appears in many respects suitable for *B. sylvarum* (and is rich in invertebrates, including other *Bombus* species). It is also not more than two or three kilometres (as the bumblebee flies) from the strong population of *B. sylvarum* at Wat Tyler Country Park. So far, however, *B. sylvarum* has not been seen in the Laindon complex. It may be that early cutting of grassland may be a crucial factor explaining this apparent absence. R.G. Payne notes (pers. comm.) that the meadows at Langdon Hills are devoid of flowers by September. However, my visits to the Langdon Nature Reserve of the Essex Wildlife Trust on 18 & 19/8/98 suggested large areas of still suitable habitat in the Willow Park and Dunton Plotlands sections of the reserve, as well as in the strip joining Lincewood with Dunton. Considerable quantities of red bartsia were in evidence, and eight species of *Bombus* (including *B. ruderarius*) were noted. Large areas of potentially suitable meadowland in south Willow Park had already been cut and contained little suitable forage for late bumblebees. However, no *B. sylvarum* were found.

It could be that aspects of the history of management on these sites, of their current management regimes, or other more recondite factors may account for the apparent absence of *B. sylvarum* here, when it is present at other similar sites nearby. More detailed comparison of the Laindon/Basildon complex with Wat Tyler and Benfleet/ Hadleigh might be revealing of the precise habitat requirements of *B. sylvarum*, and also of *B. humilis* which also appears not to occur at Laindon. Williams (1985) suggests the importance of long-term continuity of the management regime, and sufficient extent of suitable habitat as key factors.

The discovery of nationally important populations of *B. sylvarum* in south Essex has led to the inclusion of the species in the county BAP list, and the drawing-up of a Species Action Plan (see Appendix) This makes proposals for field work to ascertain both the current distribution of the species in Essex, and its precise habitat requirements. Maintaining the habitats of known populations, obtaining statutory protection for known sites, seeking mitigation where development is already sanctioned, targeting agri-environment schemes at appropriate habitat, and where possible restoring habitat are among the practical proposals.

It seems clear that more urgent intervention on the part of Local Authorities and statutory bodies is needed if currently threatened habitat along the Thames Estuary is to be protected across sufficient areas for the survival of this species. It should be noted that similar pressures threaten its habitats on the southern edge of the Thames estuary, in north Kent. Continuation and where possible extension of appropriate management of the two country parks where the species is present is vital. Further research and possible changes in management regimes in the Laindon complex should be tried. Further surveys, building on what is now known about the habitat requirements of *B. sylvarum*, should be carried out in other parts of the county, most especially in the north east, where it appears to have continued to exist until relatively recently.

Bombus subterraneus (Linnaeus)

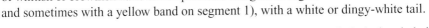

There are old records for this species in Essex, but it now seems to be extinct, both in Essex, and in Britain as a whole.

Description

Queens are large with a short coat, especially on the basal segments of the abdomen. The face is long. There are two yellow bands on the thorax, but these are often reduced and the one on the scutellum may be only a few brown hairs. The abdomen is black (often with a fringe of whitish or brownish hairs on the posterior margins of segments 1-3 and sometimes with a yellow band on segment 1), with a white or dingy-white tail.

Workers are similar to the queens, though smaller. They may entirely lack pale hairs on the scutellum.

Males have wide pale yellow bands on the collar and scutellum, whilst the abdomen has alternating bands of black and greenish or brownish yellow. The extent of the black on the abdomen is variable.

Identification

Queens and workers are similar to dark forms of *B. ruderatus*. The clearest distinguishing feature is the shape of the ventral surface of the last segment of the abdomen. This is simply convex in *B. ruderatus*, but has a distinct keel in *B. subterraneus* (see fig. 5.21). The face, though long in relation to its width, is not so long as that of *B. ruderatus*. There are also differences in the structure of the sting-sheath. Males would seem to be fairly distinctive (see genital capsule, fig. 5.32j), confusion with males of *B. distinguendus* being extremely unlikely in Essex, given the extreme northerly distribution of the latter species.

Life-history

According to Sladen (1912), the queens emerge late from hibernation, and rear a very large first brood. However, males and young queens are produced relatively quickly, so the number of workers in a mature nest is relatively small (compared to *B. terrestris* or *B. lapidarius*). According to Sladen, this species has 'little skill in wax-building' and the larvae are often imperfectly covered. The nest apparently has a 'disagreeable odour'. The nest is usually underground. Queens are said to hibernate in tunnels excavated in banks or other sheltered situations. Males locate young queens by gathering around the nest-site and waiting for them to emerge (Alford, 1975). In the most recent 'stronghold' of this species, at Dungeness, in Kent, queens emerged from hibernation in early June, workers first appeared in mid-July, and males from the end of July (Williams, 1989a).

Habitat and forage-sources

It seems to particularly favour dry well-drained, open areas, without frequent drastic disturbance, as found at Dungeness and neighbouring areas (Williams, 1988), and large areas of suitable habitat seem to be necessary. As a long-tongued species, it favours flowers with long corolla tubes such as the Lamiaceae, Fabaceae, (especially clovers) and honeysuckle. Teasel was apparently important at Dungeness. Viper's bugloss and foxglove (queens) were also noted (Williams, 1988).

Distribution and conservation

According to Sladen it was abundant in the Deal and Dover districts in most years. He also considered it common in Suffolk and many localities in south and east England. The 1980 *Atlas* shows a massive decline, with only 22 ten-kilometre square records in the post-1960 category. The most significant concentration of records is in the Dungeness area, with just two ten-kilometre square records from Essex (TL80 and TL90 – in the Maldon/Tollesbury area).

Paul Williams saw the species at Dungeness regularly between 1974 and 1988, but has seen none, despite regular searches, since then (Williams, 1985 and pers. comm.). Evidence of decline was such that Falk (1991) placed it in the 'Notable A' category, and it was included in the middle list of the UK BAP. It was included in the list of species to be studied by the UK BAP Bumblebee Working Group, but they report no new sightings (UK Biodiversity Steering Group, 1995).

Chapman reports St Osyth 2/8/1884 (White), and Colchester, 1884 (Harwood), and a more recent record from Norsey Wood, Billericay, 30/7/60 (Chapman, 1962-66). No further details are available of the Essex records in the *Atlas*, but it seems quite likely they were submitted by Alford given that this area seems to have been the source of numerous records of his.

There seems to be little prospect of finding surviving populations of this species in Essex, but the possibility should certainly not be ruled out.

Bombus (Psithyrus) vestalis (Geoffroy in Fourcroy)

This is currently by far the commonest of the parasitic cuckoo bumblebees in Essex. It is a parasite in nests of *B. terrestris*.

Description

Females are mainly black, with a single dull/gold yellow band on the collar. Segments one and two of the abdomen are black. Segment three is also mainly black, but has a fringe of yellowish hairs, which is broken in the middle, towards the rear edge. The hairs on segment four are mainly white, and those on segment five mainly black, with tufts of paler hair at the sides. The wings have a brownish suffusion. As with other cuckoo bumblebees there is no corbiculum on the hind tibia, which is convex and covered in short hairs.

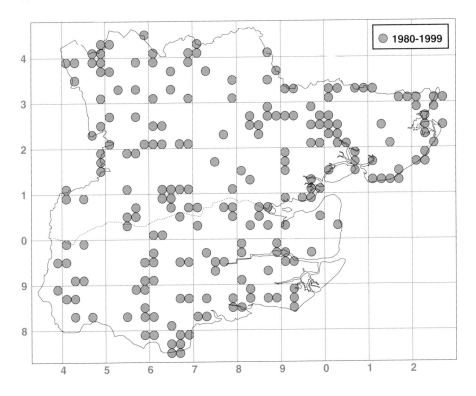

Males are similar in colour and pattern, but smaller. Some differ in having a yellow band on segment one of the abdomen, but this is a less common form in Essex.

Identification

Both sexes can be distinguished from the non-parasitic *Bombus* species by the structure of the hind tibia: generally flattened and shiny with a fringe of long, curved hair in the latter, convex and covered in short hair in the former. This feature is sometimes less clear in males. For provisional identification in the field, the dash of yellow at the sides of segment three is very helpful. *B.(P.) bohemicus* is the only other species that has this, and it has not so far been recorded from Essex. For more critical identification, the callosities on the ventral surface of the last abdominal segment of the female should be examined with a lens. This can be done with live bees in the field by tubing them, and restraining their movements with a wad of cotton wool or soft tissue. In *B. vestalis*, the callosities form a curved ridge along the lateral edges of the ventral plate, terminating just before the hind tip. In lateral view, these are less strongly curved than in *B.(P.) bohemicus*, and also set further apart at the hind end (fig. 5.33c & d). The males have distinctive features in the genitalia (see fig. 5.34d & e). Field identification of the males, in particular, can sometimes be difficult, especially in late summer. The yellow flashes tend to fade, and also the hairs are sometimes rubbed from the hind tibia, giving an appearance superficially similar to males of *B. hortorum* (though the length of the face in the latter species is a good character to use on closer examination).

Life-history

Unlike other cuckoo bumblebees, females of *B.(P.) vestalis* emerge early from hibernation (*e.g.* 13/2/98, University of Essex campus, T.B.), but they are more frequently seen from the middle of March. After a period spent mainly foraging, they commence prospecting for nests of their host species, *B. terrestris*. Their behaviour when engaged in this activity closely resembles that of *B. terrestris* queens themselves when prospecting for suitable nest sites. Females of *B.(P.) vestalis* can be observed prospecting for *B. terrestris* nests right through April and into the last week in May, by which time they look very worn indeed. Those females of *B.(P.) vestalis* which are successful in finding and taking over a nest of *B. terrestris* lay their eggs, and the resulting larvae are tended by the host species workers. Both males and females emerge in late May or early June, more-or-less simultaneously with the appearance of the sexual forms of the host species. In late May worn females of *B.(P.) vestalis* surviving from the previous season overlap with freshly emerged females, offspring of their more successful sisters. Fresh females and males continue to forage until late August, after which date the females have entered hibernation. Males congregate in considerable numbers, and follow one another in a rapid flight along a constant route over tree canopies or hedgerows (*e.g.* 8-10 individuals 'contouring' the canopy of a small sycamore and an adjacent line of hebe shrubs at Frinton-on-Sea, 6/7/99), or, sometimes, singly over low vegetation (*e.g.* over bracken at Pitchbury Wood, West Bergholt, on 8/6/97). Occasionally they take a break from this activity to pay brief visits to flowers. Similar male 'patrolling' behaviour in this species is described in Fussell & Corbet (1992c). No actual matings were observed. There are no Essex records of *B.(P.) vestalis* coinciding with the late emergences of *B. terrestris* in September or October.

A female *B.(P.) vestalis* was observed (3/5/97, Markshall, Coggeshall) attracted to the body of a dead female of *B. lucorum*. For several minutes it approached the body, moved away, and returned to it. Another odd observation was of a small tortoiseshell butterfly (*Aglais urticae*) chasing a female *B. vestalis* (19/5/92, near Littlebury Green)!

Habitat and forage-sources

After hibernation, females feed primarily on sallow catkins, making use of other plants, such as bluebells, ground ivy, dandelion, white deadnettle and tufted vetch as they become available. Though they sometimes visit garden flowers such as *Valeriana* and *Rhododendron*, they are less frequently observed in gardens than their host species. Males visit a wide range of flowers including clovers, green alkanet, hogweed, hedge woundwort and black horehound. However, they particularly favour bramble and, especially later in their flight-period, various members of the Asteraceae (such as spear, marsh and creeping thistles, knapweeds and lesser burdock) and Dipsacaceae (field scabious). They also visit a wide variety of garden flowers such as *Hebe, Lavatera, Lavandula* and *Symphoricarpos.*

Female	F	M	A	M	J	J	A
Sallow (m)	V						
Sallow		V					
White deadnettle		V	V				
Ground ivy		V	V	V			
Dandelion		V	V	V			
Bluebell		V					
Tufted vetch				V			
Green alkanet				V			
Lilac (g)				V			
Valerian (g)				V			
Bramble					V	V	
Narrow-leaved bird's-foot trefoil				V			
Misc. shrubs & herbs					v		

Male	F	M	A	M	J	J	A
Marsh thistle			V				
Mallow				V			
Bramble				V	V		
White clover				V	V		
Sea clover				V			
Hogweed				V			
Green alkanet				V			
Hedge wouridwort				V			
Marsh thistle				V	V	V	
Creeping thistle				V	V	V	
Hebe (g)				V			
Lavatera (g)				V			
Rhododendron (g)				V			
Snowberry (g)				V			
Misc. (g)				V			
Black horehound					V		
Field scabious					V		
Spear thistle					V	V	
Greater knapweed					V		
Knapweed					V	V	
Lavender (g)					V		
Lesser burdock							V
Hoary ragwort							V
Dahlia (g)							V

Distribution and status in Essex

Sladen (1912) declared it to be very common in south and east England, wherever its host, *B. terrestris* was abundant. This is still true, the *Atlas* of 1980 showing relatively little contraction in the post-1960 distribution. Morley (1899) gives Tostock, Brandon ('common') and the Ipswich district as localities. Harwood included it in his Colchester list (1884) and collected it there in 1896. Chapman gives Skipper's Island, 4/7/58 (A.C. Wheeler), Grays, 13/8/60, and Norsey Wood, Billericay, 30/7/60 (Chapman, 1962). The *Atlas* gives only 24 ten-kilometre squares for this species in Essex, but during the current survey it has been recorded in a total of 213 tetrads throughout the county, in 55 out of 57 ten-kilometre squares. It seems likely that this apparent change is the result of more systematic recording: in general the cuckoo bumblebees are likely to be under-recorded compared with the other *Bombus* species due to their lack of a worker caste and lower population densities.

Bombus (Psithyrus) rupestris (Fabricius)

Though becoming more common in some parts of England, this species remains rare in Essex. It is a parasite in the nests of *B. lapidarius*.

Description

Females are large and resemble queens of *B. lapidarius* in colour pattern. The thorax and segments one to three of the abdomen are black, and the tail is red. The wings are suffused dark brown, and the coat is short and thin.

Males are smaller and somewhat variable in colour pattern. As with the females, the dominant colour of the coat is black. In pale forms there are narrow and ill-defined whitish-yellow bands on the collar, scutellum, and segment one of the abdomen. The tail is red. In darker forms, the yellowish bands are reduced to a few pale hairs. Sladen

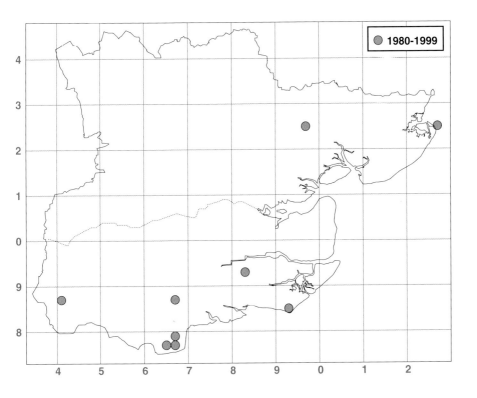

(1912) mentions a wholly black male sent to him from Colchester (presumably by Harwood). I have not encountered this form in the current survey period.

Identification

Females can be distinguished from queens of *B. lapidarius* by the lack of a corbiculum on the hind tibia, and by the dark brown coloration of the wings. In addition, they have very large and distinctively shaped callosities on the ventral surface of the hindmost segment of the abdomen (fig. 5.33a). Males are similar to males of *B. lapidarius* and *B. ruderarius*. They can be distinguished from both by the long hairs on the surface of the hind tibia in *B.(P.) rupestris*, and by the genitalia (figs 5.32a & d, 5.34a). Also helpful is that even pale forms of *B.(P.) rupestris* males do not have yellow hair on the face.

Life-history

Sladen (1912) states that this species is the latest to emerge from hibernation in the spring. It is said to seek out nests of *B. lapidarius* through June. According to Philp (in Edwards, 1997) the new generation of males and females emerges in July or August, the females going into hibernation before the end of August, whilst the males continue into mid-September. When females of *B.(P.) rupestris* enter the nests of *B. lapidarius* they kill the *B. lapidarius* queen. First female (fertilised) and then male (unfertilised) eggs are laid, and the resulting larvae are tended by the *B. lapidarius* workers. The female *B.(P.) rupestris* dies in the nest once her egg-laying is completed (Philp, *op. cit.*). There are Essex records of females rather earlier than the literature suggests (Broom Hill and Hall Hill, West Tilbury on 15/4/93, R.G.P., and P.R.H.). The earliest record of a male is 10/7/92, East Tilbury (T.B.) and the latest 3/9/82, Walton-on-the-Naze (R.G. Payne).

Habitat and forage-sources

Philp (in Edwards, 1997) gives coastal dunes and shingle beaches, downland and heathland, and other areas of open, flower-rich countryside as habitats for this species. It is said to visit plants in the families Apiaceae, Lamiaceae and Asteraceae. It is encountered too rarely in Essex for generalisations to be drawn. Males have been observed visiting creeping thistle and knapweed.

Distribution and status in Essex

According to Sladen it was then 'to be found in most places where its host is abundant' (Sladen, 1912), and was particularly common in parts of Suffolk and Norfolk. In his account, it was plentiful in east Kent, where it parasitised from 20% to 40% of *B. lapidarius* nests. The 1980 *Atlas* shows a very marked decline in post-1960 distribution, with records clustered round Kent and the extreme south-east of England

and south-west Wales. Falk (1991) noted its rapid decline, particularly in inland areas, presumably due to habitat loss and fragmentation as a result of development and intensive agriculture and forestry. However, Philp (1997) reported increasing abundance, especially on some chalk grassland sites. Apparently this recovery has continued (G.R. Else and M. Edwards, pers. comm.).

In Essex, Harwood included it in his (1884) list and collected it at Colchester in 1890 and 1893. Morley (1899) gives Wrentham, Lowestoft, Tostock, Brandon and the Ipswich district as Suffolk localities. More recently, D.A. Ashwell collected it at Bishop's Stortford in 1941, and Chapman (1962) gave Hawk Wood, Chingford (1/7/58, A.C. Wheeler) and Norsey Wood, Billericay, 30/7/60. IBRA data include a record from Ongar in 1973. It was recorded at Walton-on-the-Naze in 1982 (R.G.P.), Hockley Woods in 1983 (R.G.P.), at East Tilbury in 1992 (T.B.), at Langdon Hills, Basildon in 1993 (R.G.P.), and from 1993 onwards by several observers at Broom Hill and nearby. The sighting of a male on 30/7/99 at Lexden Springs Local Nature Reserve in Colchester (T.B.) is the first record from the north of Essex for some 17 years, and could be the first local sign of the recovery of this species noted elsewhere.

The scarcity of this species, given the relative abundance of its host in Essex, is puzzling. It is possible that, although *B. lapidarius* remains a common and widely distributed species in Essex, its population density may have significantly declined due to factors which have affected other *Bombus* species. For a parasitic species, population density, as distinct from mere presence of the host species is presumably a significant factor in reproductive success. However, the host species is currently expanding its range in northern Britain, and *B.(P.) rupestris* is also undergoing a marked recovery nationally. Since 1990 it has been recorded from all the vice-counties for which there are earlier records (M. Edwards, pers. comm.). It seems likely that this species will be observed more frequently in Essex in the near future.

Post-1980 records for Essex are widely separated in the south and north-east of the county, in only eight tetrads across six ten-kilometre squares.

Bombus (Psithyrus) barbutellus (Kirby)

This species is thinly but widely distributed across the county. It is a parasite in the nests of *B. hortorum*.

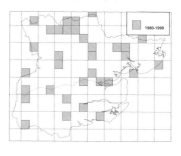

Description

Females are smaller than those of *B.(P.) rupestris*. The coat is short and thin, especially on segments one to three of the abdomen, so that the shiny abdominal plates (tergites) show through. This is especially so in older, worn specimens after hibernation. The main colour is black, but there is a band of dull yellow hairs on the collar, and the top of the head. There is usually also a fringe of yellow hairs on the scutellum, and an indistinct yellow band on segment 1 of the abdomen. The tail is dingy whitish. As with other members of the *Psithyrus* sub-genus, there is no corbiculum.

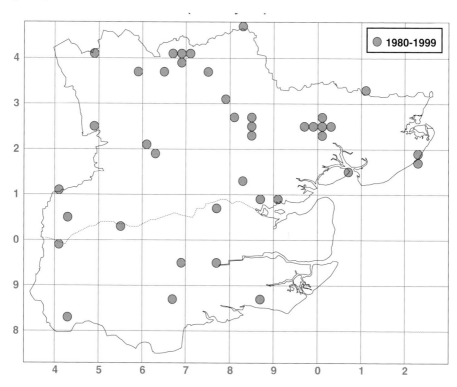

Males are very similar in colour and pattern to the females, but smaller. In some individuals, the tufts of yellow hair on the scutellum are more extensive and prominent. The tail is whitish, but with black hair on the final segment.

Identification

The structure of the hind tibia serves to distinguish this, as with other cuckoo bumblebees, from the social species of *Bombus*. The females could, however, be confused with those of *B.(P.) sylvestris*, another relatively common cuckoo. Most *B.(P.) sylvestris* females lack the yellow fringe on the scutellum, or, at most, it is represented by a few pale hairs mixed in with the black. Another feature which is often noticeable in the field is that the tip of the abdomen is curled up under the body in *B.(P.) sylvestris*. For critical distinction between the females of the two species it is necessary to examine the callosities on the underside of the final segment of the abdomen. In *B. (P.) sylvestris* the callosities are small and inconspicuous (see fig. 5.33e), but in *B. (P.) barbutellus* they are more prominent, sweeping round from the lateral margins in a shallow curve to meet in the middle as a shallow 'u', or bowl-shape (see fig. 5.33f). Males of *B.(P.) barbutellus* can also be confused with males of *B.(P.) sylvestris*. As with the females, *B.(P.) sylvestris* males lack the yellow band on the scutellum (though they may have a few pale hairs mixed in with the black). A surprisingly consistent character for field identification is that in *B.(P.) sylvestris* males the hairs on the last abdominal segment (tergite) are ginger/orange in colour (black in *B.(P.) barbutellus*). For critical identification, the genitalia are distinctive (see figs 5.34 c & f).

Life-history

Post-hibernation females are rarely seen, but are probably on the wing from late April (earliest date 30/4/93, Danbury, T.B.). They parasitise the nests of *B. hortorum*, and their offspring emerge from late May onwards. Males are most commonly seen in June and July, but in 1999 were noted at the end of August (30/8/99, Markshall, T.B.). The flight periods of this species thus correspond closely with those of the host species, except that the females appear to emerge from hibernation rather later than do *B. hortorum* females. It is unclear whether the similarity in colour and pattern of the coat to that of *B. hortorum* is a significant factor in their establishing themselves in the host nests.

Female	A	M	J	J	A	S
White deadnettle	V	V				
Bush vetch		V				
Spear thistle					V	

Male	M	A	M	J	J	A
Bramble				V	V	
Perennial cornflower				V		
Slender thistle					V	
Marsh thistle					V	
Knapweed					V	
Honeysuckle (g)					V	
Lavender (g)					V	
Knapweed					V	V

Habitat and forage-sources

Post-hibernation females have been observed visiting white deadnettle in April and May. Males are particularly attracted to bramble, thistles, knapweed and to garden flowers including *Lonicera* and *Lavandula*.

Distribution and status in Essex

Sladen (1912) found it widespread but not very common – less so, interestingly, than *B. (P.) rupestris*. The *Atlas* (1980) shows a scattered distribution across the British Isles, with most records clustered in south-east and south-west England, west Wales and East Anglia, and with rather moderate decline in the post-1960 period. For Suffolk, Morley (1899) reported it as 'widely distributed' in the Brandon district and 'not common' in Tostock. Harwood collected it at Colchester in 1913 and 1914, and Chapman (1962-66) mentions only one subsequent record (Littlebury, nr. Saffron Walden, 28/6/61). IBRA data include just two post-1960 records for Essex: Tollesbury, 13/5/70, and Writtle, 10/7/73. The *Atlas* gives only nine ten-kilometre squares in Essex for this species. During the current survey it has been recorded from 40 tetrads widely distributed over 29 ten-kilometre squares. As with other *Psithyrus* species, it was probably under-recorded in previous surveys, and probably still is. However, the paucity of records from the south of the county, which is well and systematically studied, suggests that it may be more scarce there than in the north and north east.

Bombus (Psithyrus) campestris (Panzer)

A widespread species in Britain, but with a predominantly southerly distribution, it is localised and scarce in Essex. It is a parasite in the nests of the very common *B. pascuorum*.

Description

Females are relatively small. The coat is very thin on the dorsal surface of the abdomen, especially on segments 1 and 2, giving a very worn appearance, even in quite fresh specimens. There is a dull, golden yellow band on the collar (and sometimes some yellow hairs on the top of the head). The rest of the thorax is black, sometimes with an indistinct fringe of paler hairs on the scutellum. Segments one and two of the abdomen are very thinly coated with black hair, whilst segments three to five are black in the middle, progressively encroached from the sides by a dull, rusty yellow.

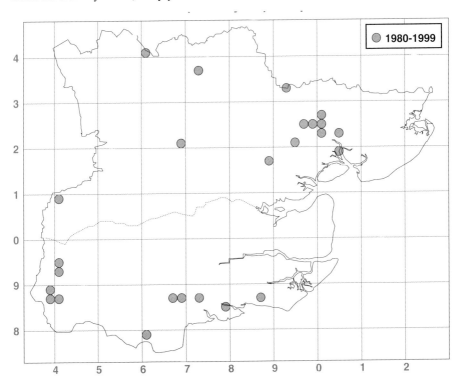

Males are very variable in colour and pattern, ranging from pale to completely black. Intermediate, darkened forms are common. Pale specimens have a wide pale whitish yellow collar, and long pale hairs on the scutellum. There are also yellow hairs on top of the head. Otherwise the head and thorax are black. The first segment of the abdomen has a thin coat of black hair in the middle, and tufts of pale hairs at the sides. Segment two has a very thin coat of black hairs, and a yellowish fringe along the rear edge. Segments three to six are predominantly pale yellow. In darkened forms the collar has a narrow and indistinct band of pale hairs, the head and face are black, as is the scutellum. The abdomen is mainly black, with the yellow restricted to the sides of segments four to six. All forms have tufts of long, curved black hair sprouting from either side of a median groove on the underside of segment six.

Identification

The colour pattern distinguishes the females from all other members of the *Psithyrus* subgenus, except in the case of wholly black forms which occur (but not so far observed in the Essex survey). The callosities on the underside of the final segment of the abdomen form a prominent and distinctively shaped 'V' (fig. 5.33b), which is visible with a x 10 hand lens on live, tubed specimens. The males are similarly quite distinctive in their pale forms: no other *Psithyrus* species has an extended yellow tail in the males. In captured and tubed specimens, the tufts of hair on the underside of the sixth abdominal segment are clearly visible with a lens. The genitalia are as shown in fig. 5.34b.

Life-history

Females of this species are rarely seen, and it is unclear when they emerge from hibernation. The earliest date recorded in the current survey is 14/5/95, near Birch, Colchester (T.B.). However, they are presumably on the wing earlier than this, as the first males, offspring of the over-wintered females, are seen in the latter half of May (*e.g.* 18/5/97, the Moors, Colchester, T.B.). The females take over the nests of *B. pascuorum*, and, as with other *Psithyrus* species, the workers of the host nest feed the cuckoo larvae. Males and fresh females appear earlier than the sexual adults of the host species. In the Colchester area, apparently freshly emerged males of *B.(P.) campestris* re-appear in the latter part of July and throughout August. A single female was observed as late as 16/9/97, at Lexden Springs local nature reserve, Colchester. Taken together with some circumstantial evidence supporting double-broodedness of *B. pascuorum*, this raises the fascinating question whether *B.(P.) campestris* may not also go through two reproductive cycles in some years. The alternative is that they have a remarkably long flight period, from mid May through to the end of August (males) or mid September (females). There are some reports of *B. humilis* and *B. pratorum* being used as hosts (Løken, 1984) but there is no evidence from the present survey of this. There appear to be no records of both *B. humilis* and *B.(P.) campestris* from the same site.

Habitat and forage-sources

The species appears to be far more localised than its ubiquitous host, which suggests that some other factors, as yet unknown, must affect its reproductive success – possibly the host species is effective at defending its nests from attack. It has been most frequently recorded in open, flowery areas on urban fringes, often in or near woodland. In May, females have been seen visiting flowers of red clover, green alkanet and dandelion. Males also visit green alkanet, bramble and, later in the year, various thistles, knapweed and devil's-bit scabious. The late female mentioned above was also foraging from devil's-bit scabious.

Female	M	J	J	A	S
Red clover	V				
Green alkanet	V				
Dandelion	V				
Devil's-bit scabious					V

Male	M	J	J	A	S
Green alkanet	V				
Bramble		V			
Creeping thistle			V	V	
Knapweed			V	V	
Buddleia (g)			V		
Lavender (g)			V		
Devil's-bit scabious				V	
Spear thistle				V	
Marsh thistle					V

Distribution and status in Essex

Sladen considered it widespread and common in some places in the British Isles, but noted it was seldom seen in the Dover district. Morley gives Tostock and Brandon as Suffolk localities, on the evidence of other observers, but adds 'I have never yet seen it alive'. The *Atlas* (1980) shows it to be widespread in England and Wales, becoming more scattered in the midlands and north. There is relatively little apparent decline in the post-1960 distribution. However, M. Edwards (pers. comm.) notes a decline in West Sussex since the early 1970s, with a current recovery.

Harwood included it in his (1884) list, and collected it in 1906 in the Colchester area. IBRA data include records from Hornchurch (26/8/73), Orsett (17/6/73), Ongar (1973), Chigwell (1973) and Walthamstow (5/8/72). During the current survey, it has been recorded from 25 tetrads across 16 ten-kilometre squares in the county. This compares with only 10 ten-kilometre squares in the post-1960 category on the *Atlas*. As with other *Psithyrus* species, it is likely that this increase is due partly to more thorough survey work.

However, it is interesting to note that despite the increase in records produced in the present survey, there is a definite pattern of distribution that has been retained. There seem to be three centres of population in Essex. One is in the extreme south-west, in open spaces on the east London fringe, especially in the southern outliers of Epping Forest. The second is in central south Essex, especially in the nature reserve and country park complex to the south of Laindon and Basildon, and the third is the mosaic of open spaces, country park and local nature reserves in Colchester. Apart from these concentrations there are a few other scattered records in the north and west of the county. It may be that although *B. pascuorum* appears widespread and abundant, it is present in sufficient concentrations to support significant populations of the 'cuckoo' only in the three areas noted. A severe limitation of surveys such as the present one, based largely on 'square bashing', is that they provide no measure of population density. In the case of the social species of *Bombus,* achieving such a measure is particularly difficult, since most individuals observed are non-reproductive workers. The only useful measure would be the number of successful nests in a unit area.

Bombus (Psithyrus) sylvestris (Lepeletier)

This is one of the commoner cuckoo bumblebees in Essex. It parasitises nests of the very common and widespread *B. pratorum*.

Description

Females are relatively small. The main colour of the coat is black, with a wide yellow band on the collar, and a whitish tail. There are sometimes a few pale hairs mixed in with the black on the top of the head and on the scutellum. Some specimens also have an indistinct fringe of pale hairs on segment one of the abdomen. The tip of the abdomen is curled under the body, and the callosities on the underside of the final segment are small and inconspicuous.

Males are generally very similar, but smaller. The whitish tail gives way to a narrow band of black and then to a tuft of ginger/orange hairs at the extreme tip.

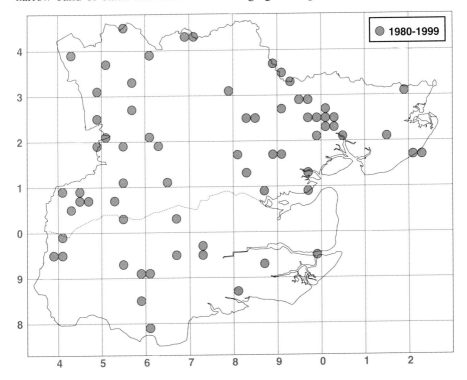

Completely black specimens occur rarely, but I have not encountered intermediate forms.

Identification

The females are quite similar in general appearance to females of *B.(P.) barbutellus*, but lack the yellow scutellum which is usually present in the latter species. The strongly curved final segments of the abdomen, and the callosities (see figs. 5.33 e & f) are quite different. The males are also similar to the males of *B.(P.) barbutellus*, but they lack the yellow scutellum (usually well-developed in pale forms of *B.(P.) barbutellus*), they have black hairs at the tip of the abdomen, and the genitalia are distinctive (see figs. 5.34 c & f).

Life-history

According to Sladen, the females emerge from hibernation early, in April. This would be consistent with its parasitism of the early-nesting *B. pratorum*. In the current survey, the earliest date was a record of a dead female on 25/3/90, on the campus of Essex University. Perhaps a more reliable indicator was a female seen at Hill House Wood, West Bergholt on 20/4/93 and another at the Moors, Colchester on 19/4/99. Little information is available about their location and occupation of the nests of *B. pratorum*, but it is presumed that as with other cuckoo bumblebees, the females of the species assume the role of queen in the host nest, and the workers of the latter rear their offspring. The males are first seen from the end of May through June. In some years, as with *B. (P.) campestris*, males are seen again later in the year (*e.g.* 30/8/99, near Coggeshall). I have no records of females later than the middle of June.

Habitat and forage-sources

There are very few records of the foraging activity of post-hibernation females, but they have been observed to visit white deadnettle, dandelion and oil-seed rape. Males are catholic in their forage-preferences, which include bramble, bird's-foot trefoil, mallow and various thistles and knapweed later in the summer.

Female	A	M	J	J	A
Dandelion	V				
Oil-seed rape (a)	V				
White deadnettle		V			

Male	M	J	J	A	S
Green alkanet	V				
Marsh thistle	V		V		
Mallow			V		
Bramble			V		
Bird's-foot trefoil			V		
Hound's tongue			V		
Creeping thistle			V		
Hawkweed			V		
Spear thistle				V	
Knapweed					V

Distribution and status in Essex

Sladen considered it (under the name *P. quadricolor*) widespread but not common, whilst Morley (1899) gave only the Brandon district ('widely distributed and not uncommon') and Tostock as Suffolk localities.

In Essex, Harwood collected it in 1896. Chapman

(1962) regarded it as 'our commonest cuckoo bumble-bee', and lists various records from 1952-60. The IBRA data include records from Fingringhoe Wick (1972), Brentwood (10/6/72), Chigwell (1973) and Ongar (1973). There are 26 post-1960 ten-kilometre square records in Essex illustrated in the ITE *Atlas*. During the current survey it has been recorded from 68 tetrads thinly spread over 38 ten-kilometre squares. It seems likely that the species is still under-recorded, and it possibly occurs wherever the host species is common.

The geology of Essex has affected the distribution of bumblebees in at least four different ways. The landforms and underlying soil types have shaped the distribution and abundance of the wild plants upon which bumblebees, along with many other insects, depend. Less obvious is the readiness with which the soil can be excavated by burrowing mammals, whose discarded nests are frequently re-used by bumblebees. Sands and gravels, as well as alluvium, might be expected to be more favourable than the clay soils which predominate in the north-western half of the county. The geology of the county has also played a role in its pattern of cultivation since prehistoric times. Since some 70% of the county's land-area is now under cultivation, the nature of the crops and the agricultural technologies and management regimes employed, will be crucial to the survival of bumblebees across the the whole county. Finally, the presence of chalk deposits close to the surface in north-west and south-west Essex, and of extensive sands and gravels, especially along the Thames estuary in the south, in mid-Essex and the north east has made possible a long history of mineral extraction. Many of the resulting extraction sites have been in-filled with refuse and returned to agricultural use, or have been subject to domestic or industrial building development. However, many of those that have remained as nature reserves, public open spaces, fishing lakes, landscape features, or simply neglected have escaped the intensified agricultural regimes which have prevailed elsewhere. They frequently harbour diverse plant communities and microclimates, and a rich invertebrate fauna. The mixture of terrace sands and gravels, alluvium, and chalk quarries along the Thames estuary supports a uniquely rich invertebrate fauna (see Harvey, 1997b & 1999a), including nationally important populations of two rare and threatened bumblebees. It is possible that the extensive heathland formerly covering much of north-east Essex, in the Colchester district, as well as the former chalk downland of the north-west corner of the county harboured species no longer present in Essex.

However, the main influences on current bumblebee population and distribution are likely to be combinations of the extent and nature of urbanisation, the pattern of agricultural management, and climatic conditions. Urban development has affected the south-west of the county to the greatest extent, with the growth of outer London suburbs. However, the growth of commuting which followed increased car ownership and speedier rail travel since the second world war has led to extensive urbanisation in centres along the main road and rail links to London. Some 20% of the county is now urbanised, and growth is accelerating. Some 22,700 dwellings were built between 1991 and 1995, and there are projections for new home building in the order of 70,000-100,000 new dwellings between 1996 and 2011. New industrial and retail development is also projected on a large scale, especially along the particularly sensitive Thames estuary.

Clearance of the 'wildwood' which covered most of Essex after the retreat of the last glaciation began some 5,000 years ago. Since that time the wild animals and plants of Essex have increasingly been selected according to their ability to adapt to the changing extent and character of agriculture. Ancient hedgerows and green lanes, often marking parish and hundred boundaries, coppice woodlands and larger areas of 'physical forest' still survive in the county as scattered survivals of earlier patterns of cultivation, settlement and land-use. By the sixteenth century, farm enclosures had already converted much agricultural land to hedged fields (Corke, 1984).

As early as Roman times, Essex was noted as a wheat-producing area, but there is no doubt that arable agriculture coexisted on mixed farms with animal husbandry, with forestry, horticulture and many other land-uses until recent decades. The large scale ploughing of permanent grasslands in pursuit of food self-sufficiency during the second world war was followed by funding regimes favouring arable monoculture and increasing mechanisation. These pressures, and the massive transformations of agricultural landscapes and ecosystems they produced, were further intensified from the 1970s onwards by Europe-wide agricultural policies. Farmers have become increasingly locked into production methods imposed by 'upstream' agricultural chemical, pharmaceutical and engineering oligopolies, 'downstream' food processing and retailing giants, and an increasing maze of often conflicting government regulations, grants and inducements.

As Britain's second most favourable agricultural county, Essex has been more affected than most by these changes. There have been large scale shifts from mixed to arable farming. Average farm size has increased, at the expense of the smallest farms (which were often managed by more traditional methods, and sustained greater wild-life diversity). Semi-natural habitats on farmland, such as hedgerows, ditches, undrained wetland, flower-rich meadows and farm woodlands have all diminished in pursuit of the large, uniform fields required by high-input mechanised agriculture. Where remnants of such habitat survive, they have been damaged by spray-drift, eutrophication, insensitive management or neglect (as in the 'flailing' of remaining hedgerows), lowering of water-tables, isolation, and by such practices as stubble burning.

These adverse changes have to some extent been limited or compensated by the protection afforded to some sites by designation as Ramsar sites, Special Protection Areas, National Nature Reserves, Sites of Special Scientific Interest, or acquisition as nature reserves by the Essex Wildlife Trust, RSPB, Local Authorities or other organisations. However, in Essex, especially, such sites (particularly the ones which at least partially meet habitat requirements of bumblebees) are usually small, and often exist as tiny isolated fragments surrounded by intensive agriculture. The establishment of larger areas as Country Parks offers considerable potential bumblebee habitat, especially if management regimes are suitably low-intensity. However, given current recognition of the very extensive areas of suitable habitat required to maintain viable bumblebee populations, such protected and suitably managed sites can only be expected to sustain our scarcer and more vulnerable species if they exist within a much more extensive mosaic of flower-rich habitats. Such conditions currently obtain (but are subject to considerable pressures) along the Thames estuary, and further north, in the Colchester area. In the former area, ex-industrial and mineral extraction sites are interspersed with small remnants of old grassland, grazing marshes and Country Parks. In the latter, the impact of agricultural intensification has been limited to some degree by large areas of relatively unmanaged land under MoD. control, extensive mineral extraction sites, nature reserves, unimproved grazing marsh, and the largely successful Roman River Valley Conservation Zone.

However, six species of 'true' bumblebees (see Williams, 2000), together with at least one of the 'cuckoo' bumblebees retain populations virtually everywhere in the county. They can be seen along open woodland rides, roadside verges and hedgerows, public open spaces, and urban parks and gardens. The importance of urban and suburban gardens for foraging, and, sometimes, for overwintering and nesting bumblebees cannot be emphasised too strongly. Even small back gardens (such as my own, in central Colchester) will usually yield sightings of all six of the common species over a season's observation. The following list is a selection of places where a locally rich diversity of foraging bumblebees (generally of nine or more species) have been observed during the current survey. To some extent it reflects the pattern of most intensive survey activity, so it certainly shouldn't be seen as definitive.

North-west Essex

This is the part of the county most affected by agricultural intensification, but remaining 'oases' of semi-natural habitat are often surprisingly rich and distinctive. This is possibly due to the chalk outcrops, and relict chalk grassland flora. Green lanes and roadside verges to the south and west of **Great Chesterford**, close to the border with Cambridgeshire host some nine species, including all the common 'true' bumblebees, and the 'cuckoo' bumblebees *B.(P.) vestalis* and *B.(P.) barbutellus*. One of the very few recent records of the rare *B. ruderatus* is also from this area. This part of Essex is so far the least thoroughly surveyed for bumblebees, and could well repay further study. Further east, and still on the county border, **Great** and **Little Bendysh woods**, though extensively coniferised, have wide, flower-rich rides. These offer forage for an abundance of common bumblebees, including the rather localised 'cuckoo' bumblebee, *B.(P.) campestris*. Green lanes, grassland and verges between **Manuden** and **Bishop's Stortford**, close to the Hertfordshire border, yielded records of all the common 'true' bumblebees, together with three 'cuckoo' bumblebees. The old railway cutting on the south-east margin of **Great Dunmow** is one of the finest remnants of chalk grassland in the county, and there is good, flower-rich habitat to the west, along the **Flitch Way** to **Hatfield Forest**. Eleven species of bumblebee, including the rather localised *B. ruderarius* and the rare *B. ruderatus,* have been observed foraging on the banks of the cutting during the current survey. Hatfield Forest itself has seemed surprisingly poor in bumblebee species, but this may be due to inadequate surveying.

North-east Essex

Broakes Wood, just to the west of **Halstead** suffered from the standard Forestry Commission coniferisation, but in recent years has come under much more sensitive management. The open rides support a rich flora and provide forage for at least nine of our more common bumble and 'cuckoo' bees. A little further south and east, the **Coggeshall** area, the **'Honeywood'** complex of woodlands just to the north of the village, and most especially the **Markshall** estate, provide a mosaic of habitats with a rich bumblebee fauna. So far recorded there are all six common 'true' bumblebees, three 'cuckoo' bumblebee species, and an apparently strong population of the local and declining *B. ruderarius*. Further north and east, the **Stour** valley from **Sudbury** out to **Harwich** supports all the common species, a total of nine species having been recorded in one area (between **Wormingford** and the river).

The most thoroughly studied area in the north-east of the county is **Colchester**, and its immediate surroundings. This was, of course, the home of W.H. Harwood and his sons a century ago. Their collecting and recording activity testifies to the richness of the aculeate Hymenoptera in the area at that time, and despite significant losses, much the same can be said today. Relics of the heathland which surrounded Colchester still remain, and the sands and gravels underlying these have been extensively quarried. Where these sites have not, or not yet, been in-filled or 'landscaped', they have developed a rich botanical and invertebrate fauna. The town itself has an area of woodland and open Country Park (**High Woods**) in the north, some unmanaged habitat along the banks of the river **Colne,** including the important **Bull Meadow** Local Nature Reserve, a valuable mosaic of rough, non-intensively managed public open spaces, from **Lexden Park, Lexden Springs** and **Hilly Fields** in the west through to the **'Moors', Wivenhoe Woods** and **Marsh,** and **Rowhedge Marsh** in the east. To the south are **Middlewick Ranges** and the **Roman River Valley Conservation Zone,** comprising important woodland and heathland complexes under military control, several nature reserves of the Essex Wildlife Trust, and sensitively managed private land. So far twelve bumblebee species have been recorded within the Borough during the present survey. It seems likely that all of them persist as 'metapopulations' with considerable movement from site to site within the whole area, each site being exploited for what it has to offer at different times of year for each species. Wetter areas along the **Colne,** or in the **Roman River** valley, for example, have abundant sallow bushes which are important for such species a *B. terrestris, B. pratorum* and *B. lucorum* in early spring. Probably no less important at that time of year are private gardens, with early-flowering shrubs and herbaceous flowers such as *Ribes sanguineum* and *Aubrieta*. Relatively long-tongued species such as *B. pascuorum* and *B. hortorum* make considerable use of such garden plants, and, both early and late in the season are particularly strongly associated with dense patches of white deadnettle which grow on rough ground and along the margins of footpaths. In May through to July, when worker-numbers of most species are at their maximum, the extensive patches of bramble on **Hilly Fields**, the **'Moors'**, the southern heathlands and elsewhere are a very important source of both nectar and pollen for many species. Later still, thistles, knapweed and black horehound are used by nectaring males of both 'true' and 'cuckoo' bumblebees. The late flowering devil's-bit scabious which flourishes on the **Lexden Springs** local nature reserve is very popular with the males of several of the 'cuckoo' bumblebees. In addition to the six common 'true' bumblebees, Colchester has a fairly strong population of the local and declining *B. ruderarius*, and all five of the county's 'cuckoo' bumblebees. The least common of these, *B.(P.) rupestris*, was recorded in 1999 at Lexden Springs. It will be interesting to see if this is a sign of a recovery of this species in the county.

To the east and south of Colchester there were extensive areas of grazing marsh. The great majority of these have been converted to arable monoculture, with associated loss not only of old grassland habitat, but also of important freshwater and brackish aquatic habitat through nutrient and pesticide run-off. However, important areas remain, most notably **Holland Haven Country Park, Brightlingsea Marsh, Old Hall Marsh, Tollesbury Wick**, and the **Fingringhoe/Langenhoe** complex, under MoD. control. With some exceptions, these areas are not particularly rich in bumblebee forage-plants, and their bumblebee fauna is relatively limited in terms of numbers of species. However, where there is a hinterland of unmanaged grassland, scrub, or woodland the species-count increases. Eleven species, including the local *B. ruderarius* and *B. muscorum,* have, for example, been recorded from **Holland Haven Country Park**. The 'rough' on the adjacent golf course, the flower-rich 'cliffs' and formal gardens in nearby **Frinton**, and inland grassland bordering the Holland Brook probably contribute in various ways to meeting the full complement of habitat requirements for these species. After an apparent disappearance, coinciding with reconstruction work on the sea wall, the very localised *B. muscorum* now seems to have recovered its former numbers at the site. **Brightlingsea Marsh** is comparatively flower-rich, having extensive patches of spiny restharrow, bird's-foot trefoils and clovers. Adjacent farming is relatively low-intensity, and there are nearby woodlands and mineral extraction sites. Again, eleven species have been recorded, including *B. ruderarius* and *B. muscorum*. Workers of both species can be observed foraging on the bird's-foot trefoils amongst the much more numerous workers of *B. lapidarius*, and later in the season the males are particularly attracted to thistle flowers. **Old Hall Marsh** and **Tollesbury Wick** harbour a more limited assemblage of bumblebees, but both are notable for their populations of *B. muscorum*. This species is now threatened at national level, and its Essex populations are small and apparently confined to the remaining grazing marsh and sea walls along the east coast. It is best searched for at patches of clover, tufted vetch or bird's-foot trefoils between the sea walls and borrow dykes. The recent discovery of *B. jonellus* at Old Hall indicates the need for further research on these coastal sites.

South-west Essex

The banks of the river **Stort** south from **Bishop's Stortford**, and the **Lee Valley Country Park** both have extensive areas of good bumblebee habitat. Stands of comfrey are particularly attractive to the longer-tongued species, and knapweed, thistles and black horehound later in the season provide forage for most of the commoner species. This area has been less intensively studied than some other parts of the county and would repay further survey work. **Epping Forest** may have lost some of its earlier quality as habitat for aculeate Hymenoptera as open areas of heather heath have scrubbed over and gradually reverted to woodland. However, there is considerable remaining open space, and recent management policy has begun to restore heathland areas. Some rides, too, are wide and relatively flower-rich. Hanson (1992) lists 110 species of ants, bees and wasps recorded in the forest between 1976 and 1990, including twelve bumblebee species. These include the rare (in Essex) 'cuckoo' bumblebee, *B.(P.) rupestris*, and *B. ruderarius*. Further to the east, the vicinity of **Chipping Ongar** has a mosaic of uncultivated land and permanent grassland, especially along the courses of the **River Roding** and the **Crispey Brook** (which flows through the town). Brief survey-visits to the area yielded records of nine bumblebee species, and no doubt further survey work would reveal several more.

Immediately to the south of **Laindon** is a large complex of land devoted to public amenity and nature conservation. It comprises the 186 ha **Langdon Reserve** of the Essex Wildlife Trust, together with the various sections of the **Langdon Hills Country Park**. The Trust reserve is divided into four sections, **Marks Hill, Willow Park, Lince Wood** and **Dunton plotlands**. All four sections of the reserve have open, flower-rich grassland, and Dunton plotlands, in particular, provides ample forage, and probably nesting, habitat for bumblebees in its wide flowery rides and overgrown gardens. So far eleven species of bumblebees have been recorded in this complex. These include *B.(P.) rupestris* and *B. ruderarius*. There are considerable quantities of red bartsia, especially alongside paths in the meadow-land and open areas in Willow Park and Marks Hill, and the habitat looks superficially similar to sites close by in the Thames corridor which harbour nationally important populations of the BAP species *B. humilis* and *B. sylvarum*. However, searches by Peter Harvey and the author have failed, so far, to find either species. Peter Harvey's view (pers. comm.) is that the annual cut of the main grassland areas may prevent the development of the 'thatch' which is important for the nesting of these species, and also deprives them of forage sources at the (rather late) peak period of colony development. However, more thorough survey work is needed on this site.

The East Thames Corridor

This is the richest part of Essex for aculeate Hymenoptera, and is of national importance. Taking both the Kent and Essex sides of the river into account, Peter Harvey's research has yielded records of 74% of the national aculeate species. Harvey accounts for this unique diversity in terms of a combination of geological, climatic and ecological factors. The climate is exceptionally warm and dry, reducing the rate at which succession from grassland to scrub takes place on nutrient-poor substrates. The corridor is geologically complex with a long history of both chalk and sand-and-gravel extraction. This complexity, and the mosaic of remnants of old grassland, relatively undisturbed former mineral workings and ex-industrial sites, supports a diverse flora, and suitable nesting and hibernation sites for invertebrates. In many sites, small-scale disturbance by rabbits, horses, and even motor-bike scrambling plays a part in maintaining open, sparsely vegetated areas for nesting, and in restricting succession to scrub. Some of the rarer bumblebees in these sites benefit from the lack of grassland management, which enables forage-plants to flower through the summer into early autumn.

Within this general area, particular sites are worthy of mention. The marshes and silt lagoons between **Rainham** and **Purfleet** have great value for a wide range of wildlife, and have an outstanding aculeate fauna. So far some eight species of bumblebee, including both *B. ruderarius* and the BAP species, *B. humilis*, have been recorded in this area. The old chalk-pits in the **Grays Thurrock** area are of importance for their chalk flora, but also still have a rich invertebrate fauna. The most thoroughly studied pit, **Grays Chalk Pit**, has been built over in its southern portion, the remainder being managed as a nature reserve of the Essex Wildlife Trust. Unfortunately, from the point of view of its status as bumblebee habitat, much of the chalk grassland has given way to scrub and secondary woodland. Along paths, and along the top edges are remnants of open grassland which provide bumblebee forage. Ten species of bumblebees, including *B.ruderarius* and *B. humilis* have been recorded. Also in the **Thurrock** area are the lagoons formed by deposition of Pulverised Fly Ash (waste from the former power station) on **West Thurrock** marshes. Nearby is **St Clements Church** tract, a site with a mixture of scrub, grassland and flower-rich ruderal vegetation. Both sites are unmanaged, and, together with the sea wall, provide forage for good numbers of *B. humilis*. (P.R. Harvey, pers. comm.). A little way to the north of Thurrock, extensive areas of rough, unmanaged grassland and ruderal vegetation stretch between **South Ockendon** and the **Mar Dyke**. These have not been adequately surveyed for bumblebees, but support both *B. ruderarius* and *B. humilis*. This area certainly deserves more thorough study.

Further east are several important sites in the Tilbury area. These include **Broom Hill**, a unique ancient unimproved grassland site which currently has no statutory protection. There is a shallow quarry and a nearby older, deeper excavation at the top of the hill, and there is some disturbance from light horse and rabbit grazing (see Payne & Harvey, 1996). So far eleven bumblebee species have been recorded from this site, including both BAP species, *B. humilis* and *B. sylvarum*, as well as *B. ruderarius* and the scarce 'cuckoo' bumblebee, *B.(P.) rupestris*. Nearby **Ferry Fields** is a relict piece of grazing marsh, with a similarly outstanding aculeate fauna, including *B. sylvarum* and *B. humilis*. However, planning permission for the 'development' of most of the site was granted in 1996, and plans for tree-planting, cycle track and amenity paths on the remainder will eliminate aculeate habitats. The silt lagoons to the east of Tilbury also harbour populations of *B. sylvarum* and *B. humilis*, which forage from the abundant narrow-leaved bird's-foot trefoil (the sea walls in this area are cut during July/August, removing bumblebee forage at a crucial time for these species).

Still further to the east along the Thames corridor are two public amenity areas -**Wat Tyler Country Park** at **Pitsea**, and the **Benfleet Downs/ Hadleigh Castle Country Park**. Much of the former grassland of Wat Tyler is scrubbed over, but wide rides are maintained through the scrub, and there are some more extensive open recreational areas. Eleven species of bumblebee have been recorded from the site, including *B. humilis*, *B. ruderarius* and *B. sylvarum*. The population of foraging workers of the last-named species in August is relatively large (20 or more individuals seen in one day). The sunnier rides, and especially ride-junctions, with rank vegetation and scrub at the margins are the best places to look for them as they forage from red bartsia and bird's-foot-trefoils. It seems likely that the bumblebee fauna of this relatively small site is not self-sufficient, but also makes use of adjacent **Vange and Fobbing** marshes and sea walls. The recent discovery of *B. sylvarum* at various points within the **Benfleet/Hadleigh** complex has led to more attention being directed to this site. The south-facing scarp has a series of open, sloping and flower-rich meadows, interspersed with dense scrub and woodland. The open areas are connected by a network of footpaths and wider tracks. The grassland is cut annually, which reduces available forage in the summer peak for *B. sylvarum*, but patches of red bartsia, bird's-foot trefoil and black horehound still persist on field margins and along paths and tracks. The population of worker *B. sylvarum* during the peak season seems to be small, and widely dispersed through the Park.Twelve species of bumblebees have been recorded from the site during the current survey. In addition to *B. sylvarum*, these include *B. humilis* and *B. ruderarius*. Again, as with other sites, it seems likely that adjacent habitat, such as **Hadleigh Marshes** and the sea walls, and Canvey Island, to the south, are utilised by these populations. In 1999 Roger Payne, of Southend Museum, discovered the most abundant site for *B. sylvarum* so far known in Essex. The **Northwick** site, in the south-west of **Canvey Island**, covers some 80 ha. It was partially developed for an oil refinery, but was subsequently abandoned, leaving a network of foundations and roadways. The site has been acquired by Safeway, and is adjacent to their store. There is some fly tipping, and motor-bike scrambling. The vegetation is a mixture of scrub, sparse grassland and ruderal flora, with large areas of narrow-leaved bird's-foot-trefoil. There are also large areas of rough grassland, *Phragmites*, and dykes.The site appears to be unmanaged. Several visits since Roger Payne's discovery have yielded records of eight bumblebee species at the site, including both *B. sylvarum* and *B. humilis,* as well as other notable invertebrates (including the damselfly *Lestes dryas* on 7/06/00, T.B.). Systematic research at this and other sites, currently being carried out by P.R. Harvey for English Nature, will no doubt add much new information about *B. sylvarum* and other threatened aculeate species.

Chapter 8   Future Research and Conservation

The survey which formed the basis for this book was conducted by quite a small number of observers. Inevitably there is considerable unevenness in the coverage of different parts of the county, with the most intensive survey work having been carried out in north-east Essex and along the Thames estuary. In part this reflects the distribution of observers rather than the bees, but it is also probably true that these two areas have the richest bumblebee fauna in the county. During the course of the survey 16 out of 17 species previously recorded in the county were re-found. The lost species is *Bombus subterraneus*, and it seems likely to have been lost from the whole of Britain. However, it remains just possible that further survey work will reveal an overlooked population of this species. The survey also revealed the presence of *B. jonellus*, previously unrecorded in the county, and it cannot be ruled out that two other species, *B. soroeensis* and *B.(P.) bohemicus*, neither of which has been previously recorded in the county, might be present but overlooked. *B.(P.) bohemicus* is very similar to *B.(P.) vestalis*, and could have been missed. Accordingly, information about these species has been included in the chapter on identification.

Future survey work could usefully be concentrated in the less well-recorded parts of the county, such as the north-west, but also in smaller 'pockets' of unvisited territory right across Essex. This might give us a more detailed (though not well-balanced) picture of current distributions of the common species, and might also reveal hitherto unknown populations of the rarer and more localised species. Future survey work might also be directed to giving us more insights into the nature and extent of the common species' adaptations to the profound changes which have occurred in Essex in recent decades. Most of the information included in the current survey was necessarily restricted to what could be observed in public open spaces, public footpaths, roadside verges and so on. Large areas of privately owned farmland and domestic gardens were necessarily excluded. Three possibilities for future work present themselves:

1.   One would be a small number of systematic studies of bumblebee activities through the year on working farms in different parts of the county. The study reported in chapter 4, carried out by Fussell & Corbet (1991) on Cambridge University farm would be a model for this, and the comparison with their findings would be interesting. Such a project might be sponsored by an organisation such as the Farming and Wildlife Advisory Group (FWAG) through their network of sympathetic farmers. A useful 'spin-off' from such a project might also be raised awareness of the economic benefits conferred by bumblebees as pollinators, and the quite marginal shifts in farm management required to secure their habitats.

2.   A second possibility would be a county-wide study of garden bumblebees, such as has already been carried out for butterflies. This would necessarily involve non-specialists, and there would be associated problems of reliable identification down to

species level. Fussell & Corbet (1992a, 1993) successfully involved 'lay' participants in their surveys of forage-plant usage and nesting sites by using a classification based on colour patterns. As well as raising awareness of bumblebees and their requirements among the public, such a survey of garden bumblebees in Essex could yield much useful information. More committed observers around the county could be encouraged to use the introductory guide, or the full key (chapter 5) for recording in their gardens. One serious defect of the current survey, apart from the obvious problem of access to private gardens, was the very primitive state of my own ability to identify garden flowers. Keen gardeners would be in a position to amplify the work of Comba et al. (1999) on the relative value as forage plants of the different species and horticulturally modified varieties.

3.   My own observations within the town boundary of Colchester suggest that all of the 'Mainland Ubiquitous' species, and at least some of the more localised species can maintain viable populations in urban areas. Rough, unmanaged river banks, public open spaces, margins of tracks and footpaths, allotments and domestic gardens, old mineral workings, parks, ex-industrial sites and the like provide a mosaic of suitable foraging, over-wintering and nesting habitats for the commoner species. In the south of the county, along the Thames estuary, such sites also provide the few remaining habitats for our rarer species such as *B. humilis* and *B. sylvarum*. Systematic observation, including 'mark and release' experiments, could be carried out both in the better-known areas, and also in other urban concentrations in the county: Braintree, Chelmsord, Hornchurch/Romford and the east London fringe, Southend, and, perhaps, some of the coastal resorts. Such studies might provide useful comparative information which might feed into management advice to local authorities and into the planning system. It seems clear that the Colchester and the Grays Thurrock areas are exceptionally rich in bumblebee species, but it may be that other areas of the county harbour important but as yet undiscovered populations. Fuller understanding of the reasons for the pre-eminence of the Colchester area and the Thames estuary could inform conservation practice elsewhere. Systematic study of bumblebee movement in an *urban* landscape could be a useful complement to the work of Saville et al. (1997) on the movement of bumblebees across fragmented agricultural landscapes. It now seems that bumblebees may travel much further between nests and foraging sites than was previously assumed, and this raises interesting puzzles concerning the 'economics' of bumblebee foraging activity (Heinrich, 1979). The uses made by each species of the diverse partial habitats offered in an urban context through the season would be a particularly useful object for study.

Inevitably, future research will focus to a considerable extent on the currently scarce and threatened species, where these still have Essex populations. There are now local and national Action Plans for *Bombus sylvarum* and on-going research by P.R. Harvey. The Essex populations (which are thought to comprise, together with those in north

Kent, a single 'metapopulation' (Edwards, 1999)) are of national importance and much is still to be learned about their life history and ecological requirements. As with the commoner species which use urban and ex-industrial sites, information is urgently required about their mobility between nesting, over-wintering and foraging sites. The location and density of nests would also be very valuable information, but despite considerable effort little or nothing is known about either in the Essex populations. The ability of this species to occupy new areas with changed management strategies (e.g. a shift from annual grass-cutting to a longer-cycle rotational system) could be tested on sites adjacent to those currently occupied (such as Hadleigh/ Benfleet Downs, or Wat Tyler Country Parks).

Bombus humilis is another Essex species which is the subject of a national Species Action Plan. Like *B. sylvarum* it currently seems to be confined in Essex to the extreme south of the county. However, it is more common and widespread within this limited range. It is a species which could be confused with the much more common *B. pascuorum*, and it remains possible that it occurs elsewhere in the county (as it did in former times). More work is needed to establish the precise distribution in Essex of *B. humilis*, as well as more directed study of its nesting and foraging behaviours. As with *B. sylvarum*, relatively little is known about these in its Essex populations.

Bombus ruderatus is our third Biodiversity Action Plan species. For reasons explained in the species account given in chapter 6, *B. ruderatus* is very puzzling. Earlier authors seemed to have no difficulty in recognising it as a distinct species, but there there seems to be some doubt nowadays concerning its true taxonomic status. There are few reliable features to distinguish it from *B. hortorum*, and there is the additional puzzle that it is observed so rarely and at widely dispersed locations. It is hard to see how the species could remain viable at such low population densities and it may be that it is declining towards extinction. It is hoped that continued taxonomic study and field survey work will throw some light on these puzzles.

Two species which are not currently singled out for attention in Action Plans, but which should be considered vulnerable in Essex, and more widely, are *B. ruderarius* and *B. muscorum*. *B. ruderarius* has been recorded sporadically across much of the county, but so far the survey suggests that it has more concentrated populations in the Colchester area and along the southern strip of the county. The species is easily overlooked because of its similarity to *B. lapidarius* in both sexes, and especially in the worker castes. It remains possible that more systematic study in other parts of the county would reveal a more even distribution. However, it is certainly much less common than the other 'Mainland Ubiquitous' species where it is known to occur, and is regarded as in decline nationally. It would, therefore, be wrong to be complacent about its status in Essex. As well as more systematic survey work across the county to get more detailed knowledge of its current distribution, directed study of its foraging, nesting and over-wintering behaviour and habitat requirements is needed.

B. muscorum seems to be in rapid decline in Essex. It appears to have always been restricted to coastal areas in our county, and it seems very likely to have been seriously affected by the arable conversion of most of our coastal and estuarine grazing marshes. It has not been found outside the immediate east coastal strip in the current survey. It appears to be still present in small numbers on remaining coastal marshes (Holland Haven, Tollesbury Wick, Old Hall Marsh, Brightlingsea Marsh and Foulness), where it is dependent on a small number of forage plants, especially the bird's-foot trefoils, tufted vetch, clovers and, later in the year, thistles. It has yet to be determined whether it can sustain itself in the long term on sea walls and their inner margins when areas of marsh inland of the borrow dyke have been converted to arable. Sea wall maintenance and strategies for dealing with rising sea levels clearly impact seriously on this species, and it must now be considered extremely vulnerable in the county. Again, systematic study of the nesting, foraging and over-wintering requirements of this species, and its ability to colonise new areas of suitable management, is urgently required.

More detailed and species-specific comments on conservation are made in the species accounts (chapter 6). There are, however, a few general points which may be appropriate by way of summary. First, there is a continuing need for careful research into the combination of partial habitat requirements of each species, including over-wintering and nesting, as well as the more easily observed foraging behaviour. Connectedly, the pattern of movement across fragmented landscapes, both urban and agricultural, needs to be carefully studied. However, enough is already known to allow of some definite recommendations. So far as agriculture is concerned, the value of bumblebees as pollinators can be emphasised, and the value of general 'untidiness' with respect to uncultivated fragments of land (ditches, hedges, field and track margins and so on) in providing bumblebee habitat. Suitably designed agri-environmental schemes can be of great benefit to the conservation of the commoner bumblebees. The emphasis should be on retention/creation of areas of flower-rich open grassland, and irregular landscape features (north and south facing slopes, ditch-banks and so on). Floristic diversity is less important than sheer quantity of the most valuable forage sources for bees: red clover, white deadnettle, black horehound, bird's-foot trefoils, red bartsia and brambles are among the plant species found to be most popular with bumblebees in our survey. There is evidence that perennial species tend to have a richer nutritional 'reward', and this points to long-term set-aside as a beneficial option for bumblebee conservation on farm-land. The widespread assumption that tree-planting equals conservation (with the added bonus of 'photo-opportunities' for local dignitaries) should be strongly resisted.

Given the evident importance of urban and suburban habitats for our remaining bumblebee populations, conservation effort should be focussed in such areas. Current successful pressure for increased building on so-called 'brown-field' sites is probably the most serious threat to remaining aculeate, including bumblebee, populations in Essex. Current development proposals along the 'Thames Gateway' are especially threatening as this is the area of greatest concentration of rare and declining species. Wherever possible, conservation organisations should be actively resisting these developments. It seems very likely that currently protected sites in this area are insufficient to meet all the habitat requirements of viable populations of the more vulnerable species. Where planners override these objections, effort should be put into ensuring that 'corridors' of suitable habitat are retained between remaining 'oases'. At the same time, experimental and carefully monitored changes in habitat management at protected sites could be attempted in the hope of increasing their 'carrying capacity' for populations of the vulnerable species. Both *B. humilis* and *B. sylvarum* establish nests and produce their sexual cohorts late in the season. It seems that one aspect of grassland management which is a limiting factor for them is the cutting regime. These species need plentiful supplies of nectar and pollen through August and into September. Abandoning annual cutting in favour of longer-cycle rotational management, possibly combined with some light grazing, could be tried at sites close to where populations of *B. humilis* and *B. sylvarum* currently exist. The complex of Country Park and nature reserves near Laindon would be an obvious candidate for such an experiment.

However, it is very important not to be complacent about those 'Mainland Ubiquitous' species which appear to be still holding their own despite massive habitat changes. It seems almost certain that their populations must have been significantly reduced in recent decades, and it remains unknown at what point such a decline might result in populations becoming unsustainable. Currently common species may well be next in line for the sort of rapid decline towards extinction which we have already witnessed in the case of the Biodiversity Action Plan species if active conservation measures are not introduced now. In addition to the encouragement of more sympathetic farmland management, urban and suburban habitats can also be managed more sympathetically. Research on suitable varieties of garden flowers can be used to build up a resource for advice to domestic gardeners as well as officials in charge of the management of public open spaces, parks, roadside verges and other potential urban habitat.

Finally, there are two key points which are worth emphasising. The first is that we need to raise awareness of the importance of so-called brown-field urban sites. These are among the most important reservoirs of biodiversity in a county so much affected by intensive agriculture as Essex. But, since the great majority of us live in urban areas, these sites are also in many cases the main opportunity most members of the public have to see and enjoy our wildlife. They have, in short, great amenity as well as biodiversity value. Current presumptions in favour of 'development' in brown-field sites must be actively contested.

The second point is that much of the potential value of urban sites can easily be lost through unsuitable management. In a small number of cases succession to scrub and secondary woodland, due to too little management, is the problem. More often, however, the problem is too much 'management'. Much urban parkland and amenity space is managed as closely cropped lawn, with 'lollipop' trees. The prevailing aesthetic is one of control-freakery and obsessive tidiness. Only more marginal and neglected areas provide good bumblebee habitat. Well-disposed local authorities who have tried to manage parkland less intensively, and foster diversity, with long-grass areas and wild-flower mixes, often claim that they meet with protest from the public. I recall a conversation with a passer-by while I was watching workers of *B. sylvarum*. He was genuinely interested and delighted that such a rare species occurred in his neighbourhood. But then he looked out across the flowery meadow where we stood and expressed the view that the council should get rid of all these 'weeds'! It is important that conservationists and public authorities alike take seriously the task of education and dialogue so that members of the public can understand and support new approaches to the management of such open spaces. The development of a radically new aesthetic of public amenity space, which tolerates 'untidiness', and favours coexistence with other species and the habitat diversity that follows from that, is called for. For this to really work 'on the ground', teams of employees who actually carry out the work of land-management need to have a sympathetic understanding of policy, and also the opportunity to develop long-term commitment to the public spaces they manage. Currently prevailing 'contracting out' of such tasks to private tender works against these desirable aims, and makes flexibility in management virtually impossible.

This chapter was compiled from information on each taxonomic group for mimics provided by Brian Goodey (Moths), Peter Harvey (non-social bees), Roger Payne and Del Smith (Diptera). Compilation and introductory sections by David Corke.

Why do bumblebees look like they do?

Bumblebees are fat furry insects that buzz. They have relatively small, transparent wings: so small that it is alleged that aerodynamic engineers claimed that bumblebees should not be able to fly.

As Ted Benton has discussed (chapters 2 and 3) the reason for their appearance is twofold:

1.   Their relatively large size and furriness helps them maintain a body temperature when well above air temperature while they are active. This extends the period when they can fly and collect food. Buzzing is associated with fast wing beats and with buzzing without flight that warms them by expending muscle energy.

2.   For reason one, all bumblebees share a basic appearance that humans (and also other potential raiders of their nests or predators of the bees) soon learn to associate with stings. This can produce a second advantage for bumblebees to look like other bumblebees: it increases the speed with which enemies learn to avoid them if all look alike. This evolution of resemblance by a group of protected animals is called Müllerian mimicry and forms a ring of similar species.

If this second were the only reason for their appearance, bumblebees should be even more similar than they are. Bees vary in size, related in part to the types of flowers they visit. They vary in colour (even within a species) geographically: suggesting a value in absorbance of heat and light at different latitudes. Most interestingly, bee species at the same location have differing colour bands suggesting a value in their being able to distinguish their own species from other kinds of bumblebee. It is these colour differences that enable humans to distinguish the 'easy' species on sight.

Insects that look like bumblebees for physiological reasons

Other large insects that specialise in fast flight and maintain a high body temperature may have a vague resemblance to bumblebees for reason one alone. If these insects also have a protection against the same type of predator they are likely to evolve a closer resemblance and become part of the Müllerian mimicry ring. There are several solitary bees that come in this category but, in Essex, only *Anthophora plumipes* is likely to be confused, even by experienced naturalists, with a bumblebee.

Batesian mimics of bumblebees

A number of insects that have no stings or other means of protection against the potential predators which they share with bumblebees (since they live in the same habitats, fly in the same way and often visit the same flowers) have evolved a resemblance known as 'Batesian' mimicry. Batesian mimics (unlike Müllerian ones) give a false message to the potential attacker 'Don't touch me, I'll sting you'. For Batesian mimics the more closely they resemble their models the better.

We have decided to include these Batesian mimics of bumblebees in this book not just to help beginners who mistake non-bees for bees; but because of the interest of this small group of insects that have such a close ecological rather than taxonomic relationship with bumblebees. Most of these mimics are Diptera (true flies) but there are a few moth and beetle species in this category.

Close mimicry of individual species

Many Batesian mimics have just a resemblance to bumblebees in general: this maximises the number of models and should increase the chance that enemies will learn to avoid them: provided the insects have a good general resemblance to bumblebees.

Some of the mimics have an incredibly close resemblance to just single bumblebee species. This may just be part of the evolution of close resemblance for the normal Batesian mimicry of warning colours. On the other hand it may be that some of these close mimics have some direct relationship with bumblebees and benefit by being confused with their own species by the bees themselves. The most obvious insects in this category are the cuckoo bumblebees (*Bombus* (*Psithyrus*) spp) which often closely resemble their social host species of *Bombus*. It is not known if the *Bombus* hosts misidentify their cuckoo parasites based on appearance or whether the close resemblance between host and social parasite is simply a close convergence of mimic to the 'model' with which potential predators most often see it.

Some mimics (*Volucella bombylans* is a good example) have several different colour forms each of which is an excellent mimic of a different bumblebee species. This phenomenon is common in Batesian mimics where it is an advantage to the mimic to be rare in relation to its genuinely warning coloured model. That way the predators are more likely to mistake mimic for model. For a common species to be polymorphic is a way of increasing the pool of models and reducing the abundance of each mimic type.

Identification of bumblebee mimics

This chapter contains no identification key to bumblebee mimics. The photographs (plates 56-62) should provide help with the identification of some species. The majority of mimics are hoverflies for which an excellent identification key exists (Stubbs & Falk, 1996). Bee-flies can be identified using (Stubbs, 1997).

Hymenoptera – Solitary bees

More than 170 species of solitary bees are known from Essex and provisional details of their distribution are given in Harvey & Plant (1996) and updated in Harvey (1997a, 1998 and 1999c). Many resemble small honeybees and a few have the same proportions as small bumblebees but only one is considered so closely to resemble a bumblebee as to merit inclusion in this chapter.

Anthophora plumipes

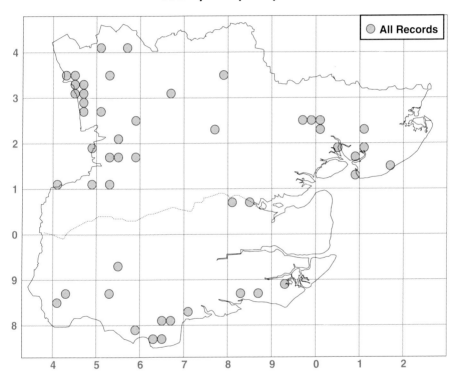

This is often a conspicuous early spring bee in gardens and open flower-rich areas of the countryside. The female closely resembles an all-black bumblebee with orange hairs on the outside of the hind tibiae and metatarsi. The male is lighter, more like *Bombus pascuorum*, with orange-brown hairs on the thorax and first two or three segments of the abdomen, and black hairs on the posterior segments. However it has a yellow face and very long fringe of hairs on the mid metatarsi and tarsi quite unlike any bumblebee species. Both sexes have a very long tongue and will visit a wide range of wild and garden flowers, particularly those with longer corolla tubes. They have a characteristic hovering and darting flight unlike that of most bumblebee species. The bee is widespread in Essex, and the present distribution map is more an indication of the distribution of hymenopterists in the county than of the bee's distribution.

Lepidoptera

Only the bee hawkmoths (*Hamearis* spp) are clear Batesian mimics of bumblebees. The scales are lost from most of the wings as soon as the moth flies for the first time, creating large transparent areas.

Hemaris fuciformis (Broad-bordered bee hawkmoth)

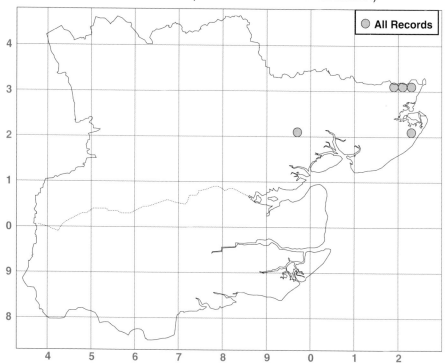

This is a woodland species. There are several recent records, suggesting that the species is re-established as a breeding species in the extreme north-east of Essex.

Hemaris tityus (Narrow-bordered bee hawkmoth)

No records in Essex since those of the late 19th century, in the Epping Forest district and Colchester area (VCH). Extinct in all neighbouring counties except Suffolk where it was recently re-discovered in the Brecklands at a secret locality. (Anon., 2000).

Coleoptera

Emus hirtus

This is an extremely scarce rove beetle, unusual in being hairy and resembling a bumblebee, particularly in flight. It is considered an endangered species (RDB 1) in Britain, its stronghold being the grazing marshes of north Kent where it is sporadically reported. It used to be found north of the Thames in Essex and there are old records for the Southend area, the last being Bournes Green/Wakering in 1947. It is a predatory species specialising in those flies and their larvae which occur on dung or carrion usually in May or June.

Diptera (Syrphidae)

Volucella bombylans

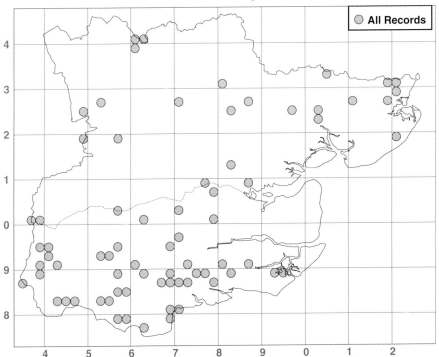

This is a rather broad-bodied, hairy fly that is a convincing bumblebee mimic. It occurs in two colour forms. The typical form is black with a red tail and resembles *Bombus lapidarius* or *B. ruderarius* and another form (var. *plumata*) has yellow, black and white bands and thus resembles *B. lucorum* or *B. terrestris*. In Essex, the latter form is the most common. It is a fairly common and widespread species, most frequently seen in late spring to early summer. It is sometimes seen with bumblebees on bramble and certain other flowers such as water mint. The larvae of *Volucella bombylans* are scavengers and predators in the nests of social wasps (*Vespula* and *Vespa*) and bumblebees.

Eristalis intricarius

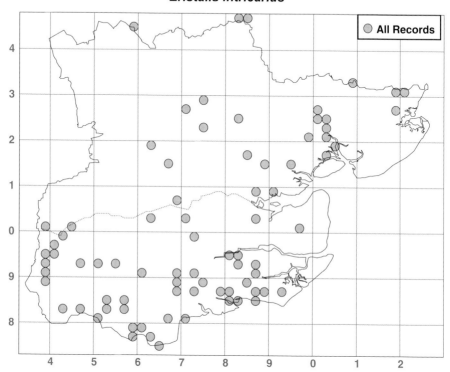

Most *Eristalis* species (drone flies) resemble honey bees. This is the only one that is very hairy and resembles a bumblebee. The females are much hairier than the males and are the most convincing mimics. They occur in two forms, one black with a red tail and thus resembling *Bombus lapidarius* or *B. ruderarius* and a black, yellow and white form which mimics *Bombus terrestris* or *B. lucorum*. The species occurs in flower-rich, often marshy localities from March to September but is most common in late summer. Although widespread it never occurs in large numbers. The larvae, like other *Eristalis* flies, are rat-tailed maggots living in shallow, stagnant water and feeding on detritus.

Merodon equestris

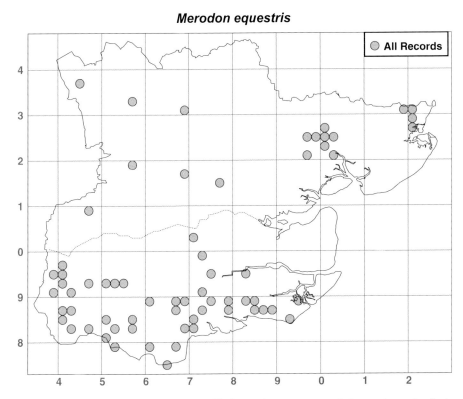

This bumblebee mimic is the most likely to be encountered in gardens. In fact, gardens are its main habitat, as the larvae burrow into large bulbs, especially daffodils. It is not a native fly and was probably introduced with Dutch bulbs in the early years of the 20th century. It is a very hairy species with a range of colour forms. There are three main forms including a black form with a red tail resembling *B. lapidarius*, a black and yellow form with a white tail resembling *B. lucorum* or *B. terrestris* and a tawny form which mimics *B. pascuorum*. Other forms are intermediate between these. It is widespread and common, especially in and around gardens from May to August.

Pocota personata

Very rare: there are no records in Essex since the 1940s (in Epping Forest). It is an RDB category 2 species.

Criorhina berberina (map overleaf)

This is a densely hairy fly which has two forms, one which is black with buff bands and mimics *Bombus terrestris* or *B. pratorum*, and a brown form (var. *oxycanthae*)

Criorhina berberina

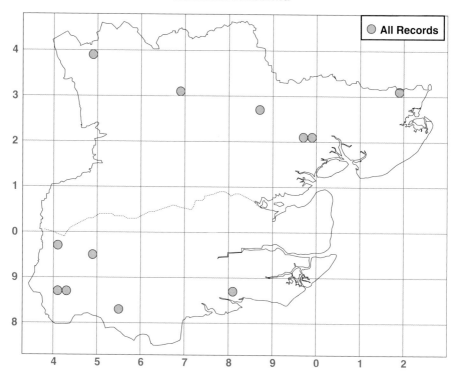

which mimics *B. pascuorum*. The species is most frequently seen in spring and early summer at the edge of woodland or in clearings where it feeds on hawthorn blossom. It is decidedly uncommon in Essex, usually in and around ancient woodland. Larvae feed inside rotting tree roots of birch, beech or ash.

Criorhina floccosa

This hoverfly closely resembles *Criorhina berberina* var. *oxycanthae* but is much less common. It is found at the edges of woodland and along overgrown hedgerows. It closely resembles *Bombus pascuorum* and is most frequently seen from mid May to early June, often on hawthorn. Larvae feed inside rotting trees especially beech and ash.

Criorhina floccosa

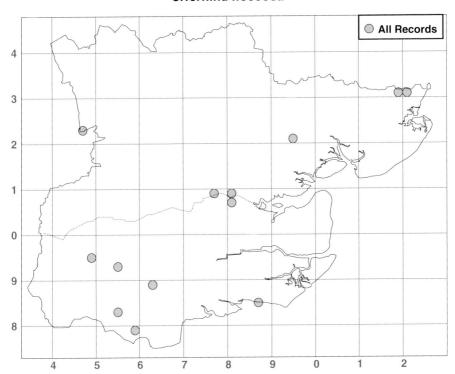

Criorhina illustrata (map overleaf)

This species is densely hairy with black, white or buff bands on the thorax and abdomen and a more or less orange tail. It most resembles *Bombus pratorum* or a small *B. terrestris*. It has also been suggested that the solitary bee *Andrena cineraria* may be a possible model (absent from Essex). *C. illustrata* flies between April and September with peaks in June and August, which is when *B. pratorum* is most abundant. Although it may share blackthorn and hawthorn blossom with its bee model, most of the time it prefers umbellifers especially hogweed, which is never visited by large bees. Its larvae feed inside the roots of hogweed. In Essex it is a local fly of open wooded areas and hedgerows.

Cheilosia grossa

Uncommon, larvae feed on thistles, flies in April, visits sallow and coltsfoot.

Criorhina illustrata

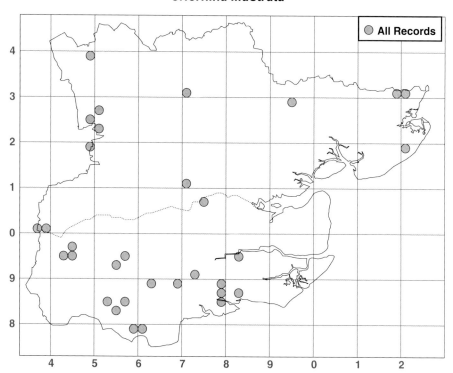

Bombylius major

The Bombyliidae are usually referred to as bee-flies due to their superficial furry bee-like appearance. The commonest species is *Bombylius major* a distinctive fly, not uncommon in Essex about spring flowers in woodlands and even often in gardens. It can usually be seen hovering before flowers and using its long thin proboscis to take nectar, much like a diminutive humming-bird. In flight it is unlikely to be confused with a bee on account of it's far greater speed and agility but at rest it is a good mimic.

Bombylius females drop their eggs in the vicinity of solitary bee colonies and the larvae are parasitic in the cells of these bees, eating their foodstores and sometimes the bee larvae themselves.

Bombylius major

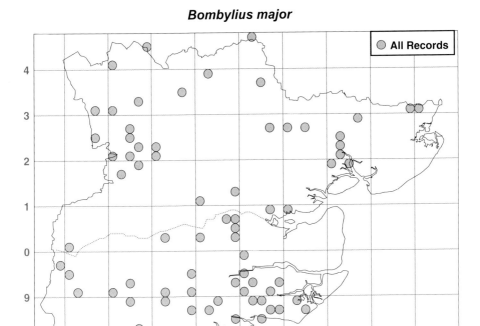

Bombylius discolor

The only other species of *Bombylius* that occurs in Essex but it is rarely seen. *Bombylius discolor* has been recorded on only six occasions. Verrall recorded it early in the 20th century and suggested it was not uncommon. The five more recent records are all coastal. Four of these occurrences were between 1948 and the late 1960s and the fifth and only recent record was made by Peter Harvey at Star Lane Brick Pits in 1998.

[Tachina grossa]

This species could well occur in Essex but there are seen no known specimens and the Essex recorder for Diptera can find no records in the literature. Apart from the south-east it seems to be generally distributed in Great Britain, with a south-west bias.

Tachina [Servillia] ursina

Only one recent record: Ron Payne captured a single specimen at the Backwarden NR, Danbury on 25/3/72. Wainwright recorded it from Chingford prior to 1928. There are recent records from Kent and Surrey.

[Hypoderma bovis Warble fly]

No records, probably once present and now extinct in Essex. Del Smith writes:

'*I have no records nor have I seen any, but as a teenager in 1964 I worked on a farm in South Weald and I have clear recollections of a labourer from a neighbouring farm with a dairy herd describing in vivid detail of how they would squeeze the maggots out of the backs of the cattle. I have no doubt that warble flies were present in Essex but with the modern insecticides I doubt if there are any left.*'

Acknowledgements for this chapter

Thanks to all who contributed records, especially Peter Harvey, Ron Payne, Roger Payne and Colin Plant.

References and Bibliography

Alford, D.V. (1975) *Bumblebees.* Davis-Poynter, London.

Alford, D.V. (1978) *The Life of the Bumblebee.* Davis-Poynter, London.

Anon. (2000) Narrow-bordered bee hawk-moth *Hemaris tityus* colony discovered in Suffolk. *Atropus* **9**: 83.

Archer, M.E. (1998) Status and quality coding of species of aculeate Hymenoptera – Part 5: The social wasps and bees. *BWARS Newsletter* Autumn 1998: 13-14.

Benton, T. (1995) Bumblebees (Hymenoptera: Apidae) in north east Essex. *Nature in North East Essex* 1993. 35-44. CNHS, Colchester.

Benton, T. (1999) Bumblebees in Essex. *Essex Naturalist* **16**: *(New Series):* 5-13.

Betts, C. (ed.) (1986) *The Hymenopterist's Handbook.* Amateur Entomologist's Society. Hanworth Middlesex.

Brian, A.D. (1951) Brood development in *Bombus agrorum* (Hym., Bombidae). *Entomologist's Monthly Magazine* **87**: 207-12.

Brian, A.D. (1954) Division of labour and foraging in *Bombus agrorum* Fabricius. *Journal of Animal Ecology* **21**: 223-40.

Brian, A.D. (1954) The foraging of bumble bees. *Bee World* **35**: 61-7, 81-91.

Brian, M.V. (1980) Social control over sex and caste in bees, wasps and ants.

Biological Reviews **55**: 379-415.

Brickell, C. (ed.) (1990) *The Royal Horticultural Society Gardeners' Encyclopedia of Plants and Flowers.* Dorling Kindersley, London.

Butler, C.G. (1954) *The World of the Honeybee.* Collins, London.

Chapman, D.I. (1962-66) The Hymenoptera of Essex. 1. Introduction and the social insects, part 1. *Essex Naturalist* **31**: (1):64-69.

Chinery, M. (1986) *Collins Guide to the Insects of Britain and Western Europe.* Collins, London.

Colyer, C.N. & Hammond, C.O. (1968) *Flies of the British Isles.* Warne, London.

Comba, L., Corbet, S.A., Barron, A., Bird, A, Collinge, S., Miyazaki, N. & Powell, M. (1999) Garden flowers: insect visits and the floral reward of horticulturally-modified variants. *Annals of Botany* **83**: 73-86.

Comba, L., Corbet, S.A., Hunt, L. & Warren, B. (1999) Flowers, nectar and insect visits: evaluating British plant species for pollinator-friendly gardens. *Annals of Botany* **83**: 369-83.

Corbet, S.A. (1987) More bees, better crops. *New Scientist* **115**: 40-43.

Corbet, S.A. (1995) Insects, plants and succession: advantages of long-term set-aside. *Agriculture, Ecosystems and Environment* **53**: 201-217.

Corbet, S.A. (1996) Which bees do

plants need? In Matheson, A., Buchmann, S. L., O'Toole, C., Westrich, P. & Williams, I.H. (eds.) *The Conservation of Bees*. Linnean Society of London and International Bee Research Association/Academic Press, London.

Corbet, S.A., Chapman, H. & Saville, N. (1988) Vibratory pollen collection and flower form: bumble-bees on *Actinidia, Symphytum, Borago* and *Polygonatum. Functional Ecology* **2**: 147-155.

Corbet, S.A., Fussell, M., Ake, R., Fraser, A., Gunson, C., Savage, A. & Smith, K. (1993) Temperature and the pollinating activity of social bees. *Ecological Entomology* **18**: 17-30.

Corbet, S.A. & Morris, R. J. (1999) Mites on bumblebees and bluebells. *Entomologist's Monthly Magazine* **135**: 77-83.

Corbet, S.A., Saville, N.M. & Osborne, J.L. (1994) Farmland as Habitat for Bumblebees. In Matheson, A. (ed.) *Forage for Bees in an Agricultural Landscape* IBRA, Cardiff.

Corbet, S.A., Williams, I.H., & Osborne, J.L. (1991) Bees and the pollination of crops and wild flowers in the European Community. *Bee World* **72**: 47-59.

Corke, D. (1984) *The Nature of Essex*. Barracuda, Buckingham.

Crane, E. (2000) *The World History of Beekeeping and Honey Hunting*. Duckworth, London.

Darwin, C. (n.d.) On the flight paths of male humble bees. [see Freeman, R.B. (1965) *The Works of Charles Darwin: An Annotated Bibliographical Handlist*. Dawsons, London.]

Day, M.C. (1979) The species of Hymenoptera described by Linnaeus in the genera *Sphex, Chrysis, Vespa, Apis* and *Mutilla. Biological Journal of the Linnean Society* **12**: 45-84.

Department of Environment (1994) *Biodiversity: The UK Action Plan*. HMSO, London.

Dobson, J. (1999) *The Mammals of Essex*. Lopinga, Wimbish, Essex.

Edwards, M. (1997) *Bumblebee Working Group Report for 1997*. Midhurst, W. Sussex.

Edwards, M. (1998) *U.K. B.A.P. Bumblebee Working Group Report, 1998*. Midhurst, W. Sussex.

Edwards, M. (1999) *U.K. B.A.P. Bumblebee Working Group Report, 1999*. Midhurst, W. Sussex.

Edwards, R. (ed.) (1997a) Species profiles. *BWARS Newsletter* Spring: 13-33.

Edwards, R. (ed.) (1997b) Species accounts. *BWARS Newsletter* Autumn: 21-3.

Edwards, R. (1997c) *Provisional Atlas of the Aculeate Hymenoptera of Britain and Ireland. Part 1*. Bees, Wasps and Ants Recording Society. Biological Records Centre, Huntingdon.

Edwards, R. (1998a) Species profiles. *BWARS Newsletter* Spring: 20-39

Edwards, R. (1998b) *Provisional Atlas of the Aculeate Hymenoptera of Britain and Ireland. Part 2.* Bees, Wasps and Ants Recording Society. Biological Records Centre, Huntingdon.

Edwards, R. (1999) Species Profiles. BWARS *Newsletter* Autumn: 19-24.

Else, G.R. (1997) Bumblebee Odysseys, 1997. *BWARS Newsletter.* Autumn: 10-11.

Else, G.R., Felton, J. & Stubbs, A. (1979) *The Conservation of Bees and Wasps.* Nature Conservancy Council, Peterborough.

Essex Field Club (1884) *Transactions of the Essex Field Club 3, Feb 25,1882-Jan.27 1883*: lxxviii - lxxx.

Ewen, A.H. & Crime, C.T. (trans and ed.) (1975) *Ray's Flora of Cambridgeshire.* Wheldon & Wesley, Hitchin, Hertfordshire.

Falk, S. (1991) *A Review of the Scarce and Threatened Bees, Wasps and Ants of Great Britain.* Research and Survey in Nature Conservation, 35: N.C.C., Peterborough.

Foot, P. (1980) *Red Shelley.* Sidgwick & Jackson, London.

Free, J.B. (1955a) Queen production in colonies of bumblebees. *Proceedings of the Royal Entomological Society of London 30*: 19-25.

Free, J.B. (1955b) The division of labour within bumblebee colonies. *Insectes*

Sociales **2**: 195-212.

Free, J.B. (1957) The effect of social facilitation on the ovary development of bumblebee workers. *Proceedings of the Royal Entomological Society of London (A)* **32**: 182-4.

Free, J.B. (1970a) The flower constancy of bumblebees. *Journal of Animal Ecology* **39**: 395-402.

Free, J.B. (1970b) *Insect Pollination of Crops.* Academic Press, London and New York.

Free, J.B. & Butler, C.G. (1959) *Bumblebees.* Collins, London.

Free, J.B. & Williams, I.H. (1976) Pollination as a factor limiting the yield of field beans (*Vicia faba* L.). *Journal of Agricultural Science* **87**: 395-9.

Fussell, M. & Corbet, S.A. (1991) Forage for bumble bees and honey bees in farmland: A case study. *Journal of Apicultural Research* **30(2)**: 87-97.

Fussell, M. & Corbet, S.A. (1992a) The nesting places of some British bumble bees. *Journal of Apicultural Research* **31(1)**: 32-41.

Fussell, M. & Corbet, S. A. (1992b) Flower usage by bumble-bees: a basis for forage plant management. *Journal of Applied Ecology* **29**: 451-65.

Fussell, M. & Corbet, S. A. (1992c) Observations on the patrolling behaviour of male bumblebees (Hym.). *Entomologist's Monthly Magazine* **128**: 229-35.

Fussell, M. & Corbet, S. A. (1993) Bumblebee (*Hym., Apidae*) forage plants in the United Kingdom. *Entomologist's Monthly Magazine* **129**:1-14.

Gibson, C. (1997) Conservation in Essex: a view from English Nature. *Essex Naturalist* **14** (New Series): 143-53.

Grubb, M., Koch, M., Munson, A., Sullivan, F. & Thomson, K. (1993) *The 'Earth Summit' Agreements: A Guide and Assessment.* Earthscan, London.

Gunton, T. (ed) (1992) *Nature Reserves Handbook.* Essex Wildlife Trust, Colchester.

Gunton, T. (1999/2000) You can make a difference. *Essex Wildlife* **50**: 4-7.

Hanson, M.W. (1992) *Epping Forest through the Eye of the Naturalist.* Essex Field Club, London.

Harvey, P.R. (1997a) Interesting Hymenoptera records for 1996 and 1997. *Essex Naturalist* **14** (New Series): 31-43.

Harvey, P.R. (1997b) *Aculeate Hymenoptera in Essex and the East Thames Corridor: Provisional Distribution Maps: 1997 Update.* Grays, Essex.

Harvey, P.R. 1998 Interesting Hymenoptera records for 1997-1998. *Essex Naturalist* **15** (New Series): 38-45.

Harvey, P.R. (1998) *The Shrill Carder Bee* Bombus sylvarum *in Essex.* Unpublished Report, Grays, Essex.

Harvey, P.R. (1999a) A Remarkable example of biodiversity: aculeate Hymenoptera in the East Thames Corridor. *BWARS Newsletter* Spring: 11-12.

Harvey, P.R. (1999b) A report on the status of the shrill carder bee *Bombus sylvarum* in Essex. *Essex Naturalist* **16** (New Series): 79-82.

Harvey, P.R. (1999c) Recorder report for ants, bees and wasps (aculeate Hymenoptera). *Essex Naturalist (New Series)* **16**: 41-45.

Harvey, P.R. (2000) *Aculeate Hymenoptera in Essex and the East Thames Corridor: Provisional Distribution Maps: 1999 Update.* Grays, Essex.

Harvey, P.R. & Plant, C.W. (1996) A provisional list of the bees, wasps and ants (Hymenoptera: Aculeata) of Essex. *Essex Naturalist* **13** (New Series): 43-115.

Harwood, B.S. (1902) Aculeates at Colchester in 1902. *Entomologist's Monthly Magazine* **38**: 266-7.

Harwood, W.H. 1884 The Aculeata Hymenoptera of the neighbourhood of Colchester. *Entomologist's Monthly Magazine* 20:211-3.

Heal, J. (1979) Colour patterns of Syrphidae II. *Eristalis intricarius. Heredity* **43**: (2), 229 – 238

Heinrich, B. (1976) The foraging

specialisations of individual bumblebees. *Ecological Monographs* 46:105-28.

Heinrich, B. (1979) *Bumblebee Economics*. Harvard University, Cambridge, Mass. and London.

Howarth, B., Clee, C. & Edmunds, M. (2000) The mimicry between British Syrphidae (Diptera) and aculeate Hymenoptera. *Br. J. of Entomol. & Nat. Hist.* **13**: 1 – 39.

Hyman, P.S. (1994) *A Review of the scarce and threatened Coleoptera of Great Britain pt. 2 UK Nature Conservation No. 12* JNCC, Peterborough.

IBRA/ITE (1980) *Atlas of the Bumblebees of the British Isles*. ITE, Cambridge.

Ito, M. (1985) Superspecific classification of bumblebees based on the characters of male genitalia. *Contributions from the Institute of Low Temperature Science, Hokaido University (B)* **20**:1-143.

Jermyn, S.T. (1974) *Flora of Essex*. Essex Naturalists' Trust, Fingringhoe, Colchester.

Kevan, P., Clark, E.A. & Thomas, V.G. (1990) Insect pollinators and sustainable agriculture. *American Journal of Alternative Agriculture* **5(1)**: 13-22.

King, M.J. (1993) Buzz foraging mechanism of bumble bees. *Journal of Apicultural Research.* **32(1)**: 41-9.

Laidlaw, W.B.R. (1931) Notes and observations on bumblebees in Aberdeen. *Scottish Naturalist:* 181-183.

Løken, A. (1973) *Studies on Scandinavian bumble bees* (Hymenoptera, Apidae). *Norwegian Journal of Entomology* **20** (1): whole part.

Løken, A. (1984) Scandinavian species of the genus *Psithyrus* Lepeletier (*Hymenoptera: Apidae*). *Entomologica Scandinavica Suppl.* **23**: 1-43.

Macfarlane, R.P., Griffin, R.P. & Read, P.E.C. (1983) Bumblebee management options to improve 'Grasslands Pawera' red clover seed yields. *Proceedings of the New Zealand Grassland Association* **44**: 47-53.

Macfarlane, R.P., Lipa, J.L. & Liu, H.J. (1995) *Bumble Bee Pathogens and Internal Enemies*. IBRA, Cardiff.

McGregor, S.E. (1976) *Insect Pollination of Cultivated Crop Plants*. USA Department of Agriculture.

Moore, P.D. & Webb, J.A. (1978) *An Illustrated Guide to Pollen Analysis*. Hodder and Stoughton, London.

Morley, C. (1899) *The Hymenoptera of Suffolk. Part 1: Aculeata.* J. H. Keys, Plymouth.

Müller, A. (1996) Host-plant specialisation in Western Palearctic Anthidiine bees (Hymenoptera: Apoidea: Megachilidae). *Ecological Monographs* **66** (2): 235-257.

Osborne, J.L., Clark, S.J., Morris, R.J., Williams, I.H., Riley, J.R. Smith, A.D., Reynolds, D.R. & Edwards, A.S. (1999) A landscape-scale study of bumblebee foraging range and constancy, using harmonic radar. *Journal of Applied Ecology* **36**: 519-533.

Patten, K.D., Shanks, C.H. & Mayer, D.F. (1993) Evaluation of herbaceous plants for attractiveness to bumble bees for use near cranberry farms. *Journal of Apicultural Research* **32(2)**: 73-9.

Payne, R.G. & Harvey, P.R. (1996) The natural history of the Thames terraces at West Tilbury. *Essex Naturalist* **13** (New Series): 121-130.

Prŷs-Jones, O.E. (1986) Foraging behaviour and the activity of substrate cycle enzymes in bumblebees. *Animal Behaviour* **34**: 609-11.

Prŷs-Jones, O.E. & Corbet, S.A. (1991) *Bumblebees*. Richmond, Slough.

Rasmont, P. (1988) *Monographie écologique et zoogeographique des bourdons de France et de Belgique (Hymenoptera, Apidae, Bombinae)*. Dissertation Docteur des Science agronomiques, Faculté des Science et de l'Etat, Gembloux, Belgium.

Richards, O.W. (1927) The specific characters of the British humblebees (Hymenoptera). *Transactions of the Entomological Society of London* **75**: 233-68.

Richards, O.W. (1968) The subgeneric divisions of the genus *Bombus* Latreille (Hymenoptera: Apidae). *Bulletin of the British Museum (Natural History) (Entomology)* **22**: 209-76.

Saunders, E. (1896) *Hymenoptera Aculeata of the British Isles*. London.

Saville, N.M., Dramstad, W.E., Fry, G.L.A. & Corbet, S.A. (1997) Bumblebee movement in a fragmented agricultural landscape. *Agriculture, Ecosystems and Environment* **61**: 145-54.

Shuckard, W.E. (1866) *British Bees*. Lovell and Reeve, London.

Skovgaard, O.S. (1936) Rodkloverens Bestorning, Humlebier og Humleboer. *Det Konelige Danske Videnskaberner Selskab Shrifter, Naturvidenskabelig og Mathematisk Afdeling* **9** Raekke 6: 1-140.

Sladen, F.W.L. (1912 [1989]) *The Humble-bee: Its Life-history and How to Domesticate it.* Macmillan, London. [Reprinted by Logaston, Woonton, Herefordshire.]

Stace, C. (1997) *New Flora of the British Isles* (2nd ed.). Cambridge University Press, Cambridge.

Step, E. (1932) *Bees, Wasps, Ants and Allied Insects of the British Isles*. Warne, London and New York.

Stoddard, F.L. & Bond, D.A. (1987) The pollination requirements of the *faba* bean. *Bee World* **68(3)**: 144-52.

Stubbs, A. (1997) British bee-flies. *British Wildlife* **8** (3): 175-179.

Stubbs, A. & Falk, S. (1996) *British Hoverflies* (2nd edn+ supplement 1 & 2). British Entomological & Natural History Society, Berkshire.

Svensson, B.G. (1979) Patrolling behaviour of bumblebee males (Hymenoptera, Apidae) in a subalbine/alpine area, Swedish Lapland. *Zoon* **7**: 67-94.

Tarpey, T. & Heath, J. (1990) *The Wild Flowers of North East Essex*. CNHS, Colchester.

Teras, I. (1985) Foodplants and flower visits of bumblebees (*Bombus*, Hymenoptera, Apidae) in southern Finland. *Acta Zoologica Fennica* **179**: 1-120.

UK Biodiversity Steering Group (1995) *Biodiversity: The UK Steering Group Report: Vol. 2 Action Plans*. HMSO, London.

UK Biodiversity Steering Group (1999) *Tranche 2 Action Plans Vol. IV Invertebrates*. English Nature, Peterborough.

Westrich, P. (1990) *Die Wildbienen Baden-Wurtembergs*. (2 vols.). Ulmer, Stuttgart.

Westrich, P. (1999) Analysis of pollen from wild bees. *BWARS Newsletter.* Spring: 7-10.

Wheeler, W.M. (1922) *Social Life among the Insects*. Constable, London.

Williams, P.H. (1982) The distribution and decline of British bumblebees (*Bombus* Latr.). *Journal of Apicultural Research* **21**(4): 236-45.

Williams, P.H. (1985) *On the Distribution of Bumblebees (Hymenoptera, Apidae), with Particular Regard to Patterns within the British Isles*. Ph.D. Thesis, University of Cambridge.

Williams, P.H. 1986 Environmental change and the distributions of British bumble bees (*Bombus* Latr.). *Bee World* **67**: 50-6.

Williams, P.H. (1988) Habitat use by bumble bees (*Bombus* spp.) *Ecological Entomology* **13**: 223-37.

Williams, P.H. (1989a) Why are there so many species of bumble bees at Dungeness? *Botanical Journal of the Linnean Society* **101**: 31-44.

Williams, P.H. (1989b) *Bumble Bees - and their Decline in Britain*. The Central Association of Bee-keepers, Ilford, Essex. (see http://www.nhm.ac.uk/ entomology/ bombus/decline.html).

Williams, P.H. (1994) Phylogenetic relationships among bumble bees (*Bombus* Latr.): a reappraisal of morphological evidence. *Systematic Entomology* **19**: 327-44.

Williams, P.H. (1998) An annotated checklist of bumble bees with an analysis of patterns of description (Hymenoptera: Apidae, Bombini) *Bulletin of the Natural History*

Museum: Entomology Series **67** (1): 79-152. (see http://www.nhm.ac.uk/entomology/bombus)

Williams, P.H. (2000) Some properties of rarity scores used in site quality assessment. *British Journal of Entomology and natural History* **12**: (in press)

Wilson, E.O. (1971) *The Insect Societies.* Harvard University Press, Cambridge, Mass.

Yarrow, I.H.H. (1986) Key to the Aculeata (Ants Bees and Wasps). In Betts (ed.) 168-172.

Verrall, G.H. (1909) *British Flies* **5**: 493-496.

Wainwright, C.J. (1928) The British Tachinidae. *Trans. Ent. Soc. Lond.* part 1: 174.

Appendix Bumblebee Forage Plants in Essex

Wild / naturalised species:

Buttercup	*Ranunculus* L. (spp.)
Creeping Buttercup	*Ranunculus repens* L.
Lesser Celandine	*Ranunculus ficaria* L.
Ragged Robin	*Lychnis flos-cuculi* L.
White Campion	*Silene latifolia* Poir.
Red Campion	*Silene dioica* (L.) Clairv.
Sea Lavender	*Limonium* Mill. (sp.)
St John's Wort	*Hypericum* L. (sp.)
Lime	*Tilia* L. (sp.)
Musk Mallow	*Malva moschata* L.
Mallow	*Malva sylvestris* L.
Tree Mallow	*Lavatera* L. (sp.)
Tamarisk	*Tamarix gallica* L.
Sallow	*Salix* L. (sp.)
Rhododendron	*Rhododendron ponticum* L.
Heather	*Calluna vulgaris* (L.) Hull
Heaths	*Erica* L. (sp.)
Bramble	*Rubus fruticosus* L. (agg.)
Silverweed	*Potentilla anserina* L.
Creeping Cinquefoil	*Potentilla reptans* L.
Wild Rose	*Rosa* L. (sp.)
Cherry Plum	*Prunus cerasifera* Ehrh.
Blackthorn	*Prunus spinosa* L.
Hawthorn	*Crataegus monogyna* Jacq.
Midland Hawthorn	
	Crataegus laevigata (Poir.) DC.
Crab Apple	*Malus sylvestris* (L.) Mill.
Goat's Rue	*Galega officinalis* L.
Narrow-leaved Bird's-foot Trefoil	
	Lotus glaber Mill.
Bird's-foot Trefoil	*Lotus corniculatus* L.
Tufted Vetch	*Vicia cracca* L.
Fodder Vetch	*Vicia villosa* Roth
Tare	*Vicia* L. (sp.)
Bush Vetch	*Vicia sepium* L.
Common Vetch	*Vicia sativa* L.
Meadow Vetchling	*Lathyrus pratensis* L.
Grass Vetchling	*Lathyrus nissolia* L.
Spiny Rest-harrow	*Ononis spinosa* L.
Rest-harrow	*Ononis repens* L.
Melilot	*Melilotus* Mill. (sp.)
White Clover	*Trifolium repens* L.
Red Clover	*Trifolium pratense* L.
Zig-zag Clover	*Trifolium medium* L.
Sea Clover	*Trifolium squamosum* L.
Tree Lupin	*Lupinus arboreus* Sims
Broom	*Cytisus scoparius* (L.) Link
Dyer's Greenweed	*Genista tinctoria* L.
Gorse	*Ulex* L. (sp.)
Purple Loosestrife	*Lythrum salicaria* L.
Greater Willowherb	*Epilobium hirsutum* L.
Rosebay Willowherb	
	Chamerion angustifolium (L.) Holub
Dogwood	*Cornus sanguinea* L.
Horse-chestnut	*Aesculus hippocastanum* L.
Sycamore	*Acer pseudoplatanus* L.
Cut-leaved Cranesbill	
	Geranium dissectum L.
Dove's-foot Cranesbill	*Geranium molle* L.
Himalayan Balsam	
	Impatiens glandulifera Royle
Ivy	*Hedera helix* L.
Wild Angelica	*Angelica sylvestris* L.
Hogweed	*Heracleum sphondylium* L.
Wild Carrot	*Daucus carota* L.
Large bindweed	*Calystegia sepium* (L.)
Comfrey	*Symphytum* L. (sp.)
Hound's Tongue	*Cynoglossum officinale* L.
Green Alkanet	*Pentaglottis sempervirens* (L.) Tausch ex L.H. Bailey
Hedge Woundwort	*Stachys sylvatica* L.
Marsh Woundwort	*Stachys palustris* L.
Black Horehound	*Ballota nigra* L.
Yellow Archangel	
	Lamiastrum galeobdolon (L.) Ehrend. & Polatschek
White Deadnettle	*Lamium album* L.
Red Deadnettle	*Lamium purpureum* L.
Wood Sage	*Teucrium scorodonia* L.
Bugle	*Ajuga reptans* L.

Ground Ivy   *Glechoma hederacea* L.
Selfheal   *Prunella vulgaris* L.
Lesser Calamint
              Clinopodium calamintha (L.) Stace
Wild basil   *Clinopodium vulgare* L.
Wild Marjoram   *Origanum vulgare* L.
Thyme   *Thymus* L. (sp.)
Water Mint   *Mentha aquatica* L.
Hoary Plantain   *Plantago media* L.
Lilac   *Syringa* L. (sp.)
Privet   *Ligustrum* L. (sp.)
Figwort   *Scrophularia nodosa* L.
Water Figwort   *Scrophularia auriculata* L.
Common Toadflax   *Linaria vulgaris* Mill.
Purple Toadflax *Linaria purpurea* (L.) Mill.
Foxglove   *Digitalis purpurea* L.
Red Bartsia
         Odontites vernus (Bellardi) Dumort.
Yellow Rattle   *Rhinanthus minor* L.
Honeysuckle   *Lonicera periclymenum* L.
Valerian   *Valeriana officinalis* L.
Teasel   *Dipsacus fullonum* L.
Field Scabious *Knautia arvensis* (L.) Coult.
Devil's-bit Scabious
              Succisa pratensis Moench
Greater Burdock   *Arctium lappa* L.
Lesser Burdock   *Arctium minus* (Hill)
                                             Bernh.
Slender Thistle *Carduus tenuiflorus* Curtis
Welted Thistle   *Carduus crispus* L.
Spear Thistle *Cirsium vulgare* (Savi) Ten.
Marsh Thistle *Cirsium palustre* (L.) Scop.
Creeping Thistle   *Cirsium arvense* (L.)
                                               Scop.
Greater Knapweed *Centaurea scabiosa* L.
Knapweed   *Centaurea nigra* L.
Cat's-ears   *Hypochaeris* L. (sp.)
Hawkbits   *Leontodon* L. (sp.)
Bristly Oxtongue   *Picris echioides* L.
Sow-thistle   *Sonchus* L. (sp.)
Dandelion   *Taraxacum* F.H. Wigg. (sp.)

Hawk's-beard   *Crepis* L. (sp.)
Hawkweeds   *Hieracium* L. (sp.)
Golden-samphire   *Inula crithmoides* L.
Sea Aster   *Aster tripolium* L.
Fleabane *Pulicaria dysenterica* (L.) Bernh.
Oxeye Daisy *Leucanthemum vulgare* Lam.
Ragwort   *Senecio jacobaea* L.
Hoary Ragwort   *Senecio erucifolius* L.
Colt's-foot   *Tussilago farfara* L.
Yellow Iris   *Iris pseudacorus* L.
Bluebell   *Hyacinthoides non-scripta*
                           (L.) Chouard ex Rothm.

Flowers and shrubs (English names) used as forage sources in gardens

Michaelmas Daisy   *Aster* L. (sp.)
Barberry   *Berberis* L. (sp.)
Bellflower   *Campanula* L. (sp.)
Bergenia   *Bergenia* Moench (sp.)
Broom   *Genista* L. (sp.)
Butterfly Bush   *Buddleja* L. (sp.)
Busy Lizzy   *Impatiens* L. (sp.)
Ceanothus   *Ceanothus* (sp.)
Crane's-bill   *Geranium* L. (sp.)
Dahlia   *Dahlia* Cav. (sp.)
Everlasting Pea   *Lathyrus latifolius* L.
Flowering Currant   *Ribes sanguineum*
                                             Pursh
Foxglove   *Digitalis* L. (sp.)
Heathers *Erica* L. & Calluna Salisb. (spp.)
Hebe   *Hebe* Comm. ex Juss. (sp.)
Hollyhock   *Alcea* L. (sp.)
Honeysuckle   *Lonicera* L. (sp.)
Japonica   *Chaenomeles* Lindl. (sp.)
Jasmine   *Jasminum* L. (sp.)
Laburnum   *Laburnum* Fabr. (sp.)
Tree Mallow   *Lavatera* L. (sp.)
Lavender   *Lavandula* L. (sp.)
Lilac   *Syringa* L. (sp.)
Lobelia   *Lobelia* L. (sp.)
Pansy   *Viola* L. (sp.)

Passion Flower	*Passiflora* (sp.)
Perennial Cornflower	
	Centaurea montana L.
Privet	*Ligustrum* L. (sp.)
Purple Toadflax *Linaria purpurea* (L.) Mill.	
Red-hot Poker	*Kniphofia* Moench (sp.)
Rhododendron	*Rhododendron* L. (sp.)
Rock-rose	*Cistus* L. (sp.)
Rose	*Rosa* L. (sp.)
Rosemary	*Rosmarinus officinalis* L.
Sage	*Salvia* L. (sp.)
Rose-of-Sharon	*Hypericum calycinum* L.
Snapdragon	*Antirrhinum* L. (sp.)
Snowberry *Symphoricarpos* Duhamel (sp.)	
Thyme	*Thymus* L. (sp.)
Valerian	*Valeriana* L. (sp.
Verbena	*Verbena* L. (sp.)
Viburnum	*Viburnum* L. (sp.)

Flowers and shrubs (scientific names) used as forage sources in gardens

Alcea l.	Hollyhock
Antirrhinum L.	Snapdragon
Aster L.	Michaelmas Daisy
Aubrieta	Aubretia
Berberis L.	Barberry
Bergenia Moench.	
Buddleia L.	Butterfly bush
Calluna	Ling, Heath
Campanula L.	Bellflower
Ceanothus	
Centaurea montana L.	Perennial Cornflower
Chaenomeles Lindl.	Japonica
Cistus L.	Rock-rose
Dahlia Cav.	
Digitalis L.	Foxglove
Erica L.	Heathers
Fuchsia	
Genista L.	Broom

Geranium L.	Cranes-bill
Hebe Comm. Ex Juss.	
Hypericum calycinum L.	Rose of Sharon
Impatiens L.	Busy Lizzy
Jasminum L.	Jasmine
Kniphofia Moench.	Red-hot Poker
Laburnum Fabr.	
Lathyrus latifolius	Everlasting Pea
Lavandula L.	Lavender
Lavatera	Tree Mallow
Ligustrum L.	Privet
Linaria purpurea (L.)	Purple Toadflax
Lobelia L.	
Lonicera L.	Honeysuckle
Mahonia	
Narcissus	Daffodil
Passiflora	Passion Flower
Petunia	
Rhododendron L.	
Ribes sanguineum Pursh.	Flowering Currant
Rosa L.	Roses
Rosmarinus officinalis L.	Rosemary
Salvia L.	Sage
Symphoricarpos Duhamel	Snowberry
Syringa L.	Lilac
Thymus L.	Thymes
Valeriana L.	Valerian
Verbena L.	
Viburnum L.	
Viola L.	Pansies and Violets

Agricultural crops:

Oil-seed Rape	*Brassica napus* L.
Field Bean	*Vicia faba* L

Species Index

Note: *This index includes only the page references to the start of each species account (not every mention of the species in the book). These references are given in* roman type. *In addition, the colour plate illustrations are given in* **bold type.**